*Hebridean Healers*

# HEBRIDEAN HEALERS
## *The Beatons of Mull*

Christine Leach, Andrea Cameron,
Elizabeth Carter and Miek Zwamborn

ORIGIN

First published in 2024 by Origin
an imprint of Birlinn Ltd
West Newington House
10 Newington Road
Edinburgh
EH9 1QS
www.birlinn.co.uk

Design and layout by Mark Blackadder and Tom Johnstone

ISBN: 978 1 83983 052 5

British Library Cataloguing in Publication Data
A catalogue record for this book is available from the British Library

Printed and bound in Great Britain by
Bell & Bain Ltd., Glasgow

FSC
www.fsc.org

MIX
Paper | Supporting
responsible forestry
FSC® C007785

# Contents

# Introduction

# *The Beatons of Pennycross:*
# *How the Search Began*

Just beyond Pennyghael, on a narrow strip of land between the old track from Craignure to Iona and the shore line of Loch Scridain, lies an overgrown plot within traces of an ancient moss-covered wall. It is silent and hidden for most of the year under a blanket of bracken. It is only in the winter that the outline can be seen of what was a medieval herb garden.

There are only a few trees here now, remaining survivors of a windbreak planted in the Middle Ages, and before that, the mixture of Atlantic hazel, oak and ash, willow and rowan, whose origins date back to the last Ice Age. At first glance, the trees seem to be dead or dying but, in the spring, as life quickens, buds appear on ancient branches, and the

The extent of the ancient Beaton Physic garden looking south east. The belt of sheltering trees is to the left of the photo, the modern fence indicating the fact that the area is owned by two different proprietors (photo by Christine Leach).

The garden site in summer, under its blanket of bracken (photo by Christine Leach).

old oak, which crashed to the ground many centuries ago, is sprouting and growing again from its recumbent trunk.

Nearly 500 years ago this medicinal garden was so famous that visitors came by sea to visit the practitioners who established it and used it regularly. And so it is that we enter the world of wormwood, sweet violet, thyme and foxglove and a dynasty of doctors – the Beatons. Exactly what they grew we don't know, though we can surmise, based on historical evidence of the use of plants at the time. Only the soil itself remembers roots, stems, leaves and flowers which once brought shade and colour, perfume and healing. It is now far too long ago for buried seeds to germinate and reveal what herbs were cultivated here.

Although the garden is long gone, happily, there is other proof of the Beatons' close relationship with the island of Mull; the manuscripts they painstakingly wrote and treasured so carefully; the stories about their treatments which were so memorable that they were handed down by patients and islanders to the present day; the medical procedures, no longer performed, but which were the precursors of modern practice; and the herbal remedies, some of which are still in use today.

Somehow, despite the garden's invisibility, it still speaks to the imagination. As you stand among the old gnarled trunks in the Shelter Belt and hear a blackbird call or wander among the remnants of dead bracken, you can almost see it flourish, almost see one of the physicians bending down to tend a plant, pluck fresh leaves to make a cordial or an ointment.

And it is here, in the garden, that our story began.

# 1

# *Finding the Background Story*

## The Beatons' Place in Scottish History

### The Vikings and Their Hebridean Legacy, Duns and Birlinns

To begin the story of the physicians who lived and worked at Pennycross we need to go back and find where they fitted into Scottish history. The Beaton doctors were hereditary physicians to the Lords of the Isles and through this connection served in the courts of the kings of Scotland for over 300 years. They treated rich and poor alike, and became eminent physicians in the Western Highlands and Islands of Scotland.

Their story in the Hebrides begins with these great Lords of the Isles, chiefs of Clan Donald who rose up to vanquish the Viking invaders and drive them from their lands. After a century of raids and sporadic settlement the Viking tide had finally engulfed the area in the middle of the ninth century. Under Norse control they colonised the Inner and Outer Hebrides, and over time many invaders married into the local population. From this

mixed race of peoples, the later clans of the Western Isles evolved.

The Hebrides and southern half of the Kintyre Peninsula remained tributaries of Norway until 1140, when there was a Gaelic revival under the Celtic warrior Somerled, which led to over 120 years of battles and skirmishes. The western lords were very skilled sailors and their birlinn galleys gave them the status of a formidable sea-power. In the late Middle Ages, the Lords of the Isles were known to maintain the largest birlinn fleet in the Hebrides. Sea battles were a way of life, central to the Gaelic resurgence against the Vikings.

The birlinn was a wooden vessel propelled by both sail and oar. It was a clinker-built, open-hulled craft, with high prow and stern, that could be either sailed or rowed. The central mast carried a square or rectangular sail and seating could accommodate from twelve to eighteen rowers, depending on the size of the vessel. The name may derive from the

Image from *Miscellany on the Life of St Edmund* (Morgan Library).

Norse *byroingr* – 'ship of burthen'.[1] Certainly birlinns show a marked Viking influence and are assumed to have been direct descendants of the Viking longships, with a continuous tradition of construction and use from the time the Scandinavians first appeared in Britain and Ireland in the ninth century. There was relatively little modification of their basic design for several hundred years, so it is not unreasonable to assume that they were good at the jobs they were designed for.

Because the birlinn could be rowed as well as sailed, it had considerable versatility, and it is probable that an experienced crew could row themselves away from any threat posed by larger, more cumbersome craft. A shallow draught made the birlinn ideal for beaching, for being manoeuvred in amongst rocks and also for being taken up river. Size and lightness relative to crew numbers meant that it could easily be taken out of the water and transported over land from one stretch of water to another. It could carry relatively large numbers of men and also booty on the return voyages.

The birlinn was also an excellent vessel for trading activities. There were mercantile centres on Islay, Gigha, Kintyre and Knapdale,

Model of Birlinn, created by Philip Siddall.

Three examples of the lymphad used as heraldic emblem: top, the heraldic galley; bottom left, arms of MacDonald of MacDonald; bottom right, arms of Maclean of Duart and Morven (Wikimedia).

and in the fourteenth century there was constant trade between the Western Isles, Ireland and England under the patronage of local lords. These versatile vessels could be used for fishing, cattle-transport and general trading, apart from their primary function of warfare and troop-carrying. It is interesting to note that, very close to the site of the Beaton land at Pennycross on Mull, is a small cove called Port na Birlinne, indicating perhaps that it was suitable for birlinns to use.

No significant fragments of original vessels survive, and contemporary documentation does little to describe their characteristics or manufacture. The main sources of information are representations found on heraldic seals, West Highland crosses and grave slabs. The birlinn appears in Scottish heraldry as the 'lymphad' – a corruption of the Gaelic *long-fhada* – longship. It is a single-masted ship propelled by oars. In addition to the mast and oars, the lymphad had three flags and a basket, although the actual ships never sported either the baskets or the fore and aft castles. The lymphad usually indicated some title associated with islands, specifically those on the west coast of Scotland, including the Hebrides, such as the Lord of the Isles.

In 1156 Somerled set out with 80 galleys to intercept the Viking Godred of Man, who was sailing north to lay claim to the southern Hebrides. A great sea battle took place off Islay; the fighting continued through the night until dawn revealed the Norse fleet broken and the Gaelic force too badly

Two funerary monuments incorporating the lymphad. Above, a fine example on the shaft of an early sixteenth-century cross from Pennygown burial ground, Isle of Mull (photo by Dr W. Clegg, Isle of Mull Museum). Below, a graveslab from Iona (from H.D. Graham, *Antiquities of Iona*, 1850).

Battle of Largs, 1263, detail from the painting by William Hole, c.1899 (Scottish National Portrait Gallery, public domain, via Wikimedia Commons).

mauled to follow up their victory. A fragile truce was agreed which Somerled broke two years later by invading the Isle of Man and claiming ownership of the southern Hebrides, including Mull, for himself.[2]

Somerled's descendants continued to lead the Gaelic clans gathered from across the isles and his grandson Donald gave his name to Clan Donald (MacDonald). Over time the MacDonalds not only resented Norwegian authority over the Western Isles, but also the Scottish Kings over-lordship.

A decisive land and sea battle, the Battle of Largs, took place in 1263 at Largs and the Norwegian kings were forced to renounce their sovereignty. The Viking King Haakon had sailed south from Norway with a large fleet of between 120 to 200 galleys to pursue his claim to Arran and Bute. They sailed through the Sound of Mull and anchored off Kerrera island near Oban, from where they sent smaller birlinn fleets to plunder the land and subdue the Scottish lords. Haakon then moved on and set up his headquarters at Gigha where he ordered his lords to go 'reiving' (raiding and plundering cattle and other goods) to obtain supplies. Over 60 birlinn ships sailed up Loch Long and were hauled overland to Loch Lomond to plunder the islands and raid as far as the Stirling plain.[3] The MacDonalds performed well during the battle and from this time the clan grew in power. Through inheritance, marriage and the fortunate decision to back Robert the Bruce during the Scottish Wars of Independence, they came to control a vast dominion in the west and began to style themselves the Lords of the Isles.[4]

The Lords used the coastline to their advantage, strategically siting their castles overlooking bays and anchorages to protect their galleys. Some castle harbours like Dunyvaig on Islay and Claig on Jura were capable of holding huge galley fleets, consolidating power and giving status to the clan chiefs.

The location of the castles at intervals along the coast allowed beacon fires to be readily seen and warning signals to be passed between the clans. A beacon fire lit at Dunollie in Oban could be seen at Duart on Mull and from there passed to Coeffin on Lismore, then Glensanda and on up Loch Linnhe. Large fleets of birlinns were a common sight for the people who inhabited the Western Isles.

On the coasts of Loch Scridain, Isle of Mull, there are the remains of a string of Iron Age duns. These were comparatively small defensive enclosures with thick dry-stone walls; each had an associated farming settlement with the people being engaged in simple

A Scottish dun (from Jackie Le May, *Ardmeanach, A Hidden Corner of Mull*, The New Iona Press, 1992).

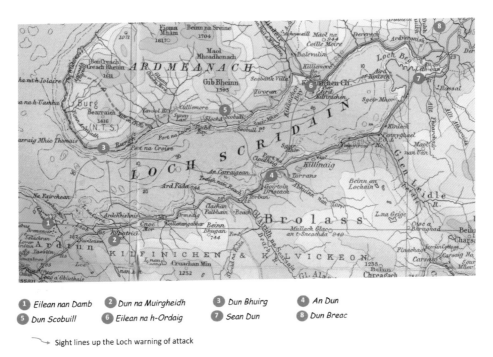

1 Eilean nan Damb   2 Dun na Muirgheidh   3 Dun Bhuirg   4 An Dun
5 Dun Scobuill   6 Eilean na h-Ordaig   7 Sean Dun   8 Dun Breac

↳ Sight lines up the Loch warning of attack

Iron Age duns around the coast of Loch Scridain, Isle of Mull (map base reproduced with permission of the National Library of Scotland).

agriculture and stock rearing. Nothing survives of the people's wattle and daub huts, but the remains of the duns themselves are still to be seen. Each dun was within signalling distance of the next. As soon as signs of approaching Viking vessels appeared on the horizon, a beacon fire would have been lit at the first dun, and the warning relayed down the Loch in a remarkably short time.

The administrative centre of the Lordship, where the Council met, was Finlaggan Island on Islay. The Stewart dynasty had succeeded to the throne of Scotland by 1371 and the MacDonald Chief, John of Islay, had come to control a vast dominion in the west and began formally to style himself 'Lord of the Isles'. Under his leadership 16 members convened around the great stone table of Mac-Donald to agree policy on how to govern the Gaelic principality. They consisted of the chieftains of a number of vassal clans; among these were close or distant relatives of the Lord, including the Macleans of Mull and other families who served the MacDonalds. During the period of the Lordship which ran from 1350 to 1493, the entire Hebrides and the West Highland coastal area formed a single Atlantic principality.[5]

## The Arrival of the Beaton Clan in Scotland

Angus Og, grandson of Donald, founder of the MacDonald clan, married Agnes O'Cahan in *c*.1300. She was the daughter of the Lord of Limvady who ruled in County Derry, Ireland. Her dowry included 140 men taken from every clan in the O'Cahan territory. Among these were men from the Beaton clan, reputedly part of the O'Neal tribe, who were already known in Ireland for their exceptional learning and medical knowledge. The Beatons travelled from Ireland with this retinue and went on to become hereditary physicians to the Lords of the Isles.[6]

The earliest Beaton on record in Scotland was Patrick MacBeth, principal physician to Robert the Bruce (Robert I) who ruled Scotland from 1306 to 1329. It is not surprising to find a Beaton among the royal household at this time, given the close association between Robert the Bruce and Angus Og.[7] In 1306 Robert the Bruce's fight for the Scottish Crown lay in tatters, he was ambushed near Tyndrum and fled west. Angus Og protected Bruce in his castles at Saddell and Dunavertie, eventually moving him by boat to Rathlin Island to hide out the winter. While Angus Og was heavily involved in supporting Robert the Bruce's claim to the Scottish throne, he was

MacDonald of the Isles (from R.R. Mclan, *The Clans of the Scottish Highlands*, 1845).

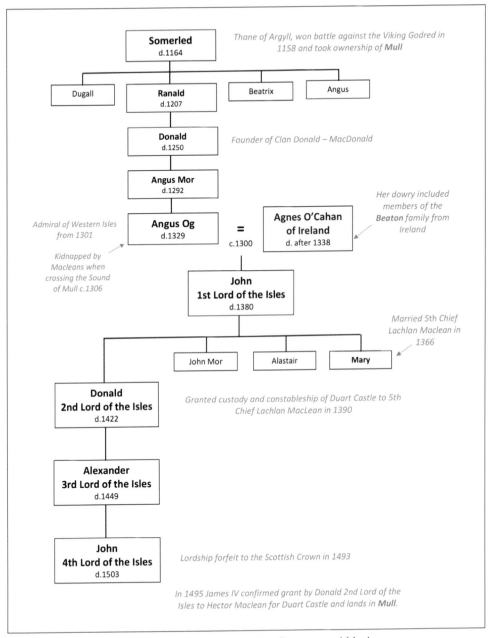

Pedigree of the Lords of the Isles, Beatons and Macleans.

Ruins of Duard Castle (from J.P. Maclean, *A History of the Clan Maclean*, 1889).

sailing amongst the Hebridean Islands and the coast pressing this claim, frequently involved in skirmishes with enemies of the Bruce. On one occasion he was crossing the Sound of Mull to Aros Castle, when he was kidnapped by the Macleans of Mull who held him captive in Dunstaffnage Castle. The Macleans at that time were opponents of Robert the Bruce and they thought that capturing Angus Og would buy them favour with the House of Lorne, also enemies of the Bruce. The Macleans soon realised that instead they were considered overbold and would likely be punished for their forwardness and insolence. Angus Og took advantage of this situation and persuaded the Macleans to switch sides; taking him at his word they did so and all escaped back to Mull. As reward Angus Og gave land to Hector Maclean and made his brother, Lachlan, Chamberlain of his household, an honourable position responsible for domestic and financial affairs. Thus, the bonds between the two families were formed and grew strong. In 1314 Angus Og played a major part in the Scottish victory at Bannockburn. His loyalty to Robert the Bruce was rewarded with lands and titles as well as the trust and counsel of the King.[8] Lachlan Maclean married the granddaughter of Angus Og in 1366 and through this marriage Lachlan acquired new lands in Morvern and was allowed to continue living in Duart Castle. During the seventeenth and eighteenth centuries the Macleans repeatedly lost ownership of the castle to the Earl of Argyll. It then fell into disrepair until it was purchased by the Maclean family in the early twentieth century and it remains the family seat to the present day.

It is reasonable to assume that Beatons visited Mull as members of the household of Angus Og in the early 1300s, and this association with the Macleans led to the eventual settlement of at least two branches of Beatons on the island and their future position as physicians to Clan Maclean. Having married into Clan MacDonald, Clan Maclean was given special favour by the Lords of the Isles. This caused jealousy amongst other leading families, as is illustrated by an event in 1460 when a great feast was held at Aros Castle on Mull.

As Chamberlain, Maclean's role was to seat all the principal men by rank, but on this occasion, he was tricked into allowing someone else to carry out this duty. As a result, he was promptly and publicly excluded from his rightful seat at the table causing him to leave in a rage. Interestingly, records describing this event show that 'Beatton the principal physician' was included at the table and asked to sit down immediately after the high-ranking Lairds had been named. Gaelic law tracts in AD 600 to 700 on status in society did not rank a physician as highly as a poet, however during the feast at Aros, Beaton was seated ahead of MacMhuirich the poet. This helps illustrate the renown of the Beaton medical kindred, obtained, one would assume, through their great skill and

Aros Castle, Isle of Mull, an aquatint engraving by William Daniell (from *A Voyage round the Coasts of Britain*, 1815-18).

# The Beaton Name

In this volume, for the sake of simplicity and clarity, the Anglicised version of the name is used throughout. One of the things which assists in tracing the early Beatons in surviving documents is the rarity of their name. Originally in the Gaelic form of MacMeic-bethad, it had shortened by the sixteenth century to MacBethadh or MacBeatha, while in the Scots form it became MacBeth or MacBeath. Sometime in the late sixteenth century the kindred began to adopt Beaton as the surname used in non-Gaelic contexts, although this was never adopted in Ireland. There is often confusion over the origins of the Beaton medical kindred because of a Lowland family also called Beaton who originated in France and often used the French form Béthune, however the link between the two families is the subject of scholarly conjecture.

The genealogy of the Beaton families also reveals that there was no apparent connection between the medical kindred and MacBeth, the eleventh-century Scottish king, despite the shared name of 'son of life'.

gained during their first 200 years living in the Hebrides.[9]

The Beatons practiced medicine in Scotland from the early 1300s to the 1700s. They were well educated at leading European medical universities and combined this knowledge with their herbal lore to effect successful cures, which earned great renown. Gaelic stories and anecdotes about health often included a Beaton, known to be doctors to the Kings of Scotland and the Lords of the Isles. Their status and the circles in which they moved meant they also tended to marry into learned or professional families.

The earliest record of a Beaton living in the Hebrides is on Islay, principal seat of the Lords of the Isles; this comes from a land grant in 1408. The earliest record of a Beaton living on Mull is 1572, as described in a grant for the land at Pennycross made by Hector Maclean to his servant in the office of principal surgeon, or in Gaelic *Ollamh Muileach*.[10] The Islay branch of the Beaton family remained the most senior, even after the Lordship of the Isles had diminished, as demonstrated in a land grant by James VI to Fergus Macbeth 'chief physician within the bounds of the Islands of Scotland' in 1609.[11]

The Beaton doctors settled on the islands of Islay, Mull, Bute, Skye and Colonsay, also the mainland as far as Angus during the fifteenth century. They are also recorded living on North and South Uist during the 1600s. Some members of the family became seannachies (bards and genealogists) and were famous in Mull and the Outer Hebrides for their clan pedigrees and libraries of unique literary works.[12] Perhaps it is worth noting that much of the preservation of Maclean clan history may be attributed to members of the Beaton kindred, who had become their *Seanchaidhean* (Seannachie in Scottish Gaelic) as well as their physicians.

Every Scottish monarch from Robert I to James VI is believed to have had a Beaton physician in attendance. In 1527 a description of Gaelic learned orders prepared for King James V specifically singles out the profession of medicine, stating that 'thay ar richt excellent in it'. It can be demonstrated through examination of the payroll of the crown that there were Beaton doctors, often more than one, present in the Royal court from Robert I (1306 to 1329) to Charles I (1625 to 1649), therefore it is reasonable to conclude this high praise referred to the Beaton medical kindred.[13]

Ultimately the MacDonald clan were too greedy for land and became involved in many skirmishes with the Scottish crown, on occasion entering into conspiracy with the English kings. By 1493 John, 4th Lord of the Isles, proved incapable of controlling his clansmen and the Lordship was formally forfeited to the Scottish crown. The MacDonald, Maclean and other vassal clans continued on in their strongholds defending the lands they owned, acquiring more when the opportunity arose. The Lordship had been a model of Highland society of those times, rigidly structured but supportive of the arts and learning, where medical men and poets were rewarded with land grants and funded in their formal education. It is said that the Scots Court of Session, established in 1532 and known as the 'auld fifteen', was modelled on the Finlaggan procedure where the Lords met around a huge stone table.

The Beaton doctors continued to build on their reputation, spreading into the Outer Hebrides and continuing to practise for a further 250 years. Although the Islay branch was the oldest and most senior, the Mull branch at Pennycross rose in prominence and became one of the best-known medical families of the seventeenth century.[14]

## The Medical Culture the Beatons Inherited

The origins of medicine may be summed up as: trial and error; cure or blunder; health or sickness; life or death. The sources of knowledge of both diseases and cures, remedies and poisons, would have come from millennia of experimentation, enquiry, accident, pure chance and instances of insight or genius, gradually leading to a store of learning and

Left, puffball, similar to those excavated at Skara Brae, Orkney (photo by Henryk Nietrój, public domain); right, sphagnum moss (photo by Miek Zwamborn).

experience handed down from generation to generation.

## Prehistoric Medicine

To understand the medical tradition inherited by the Beaton physicians, it is necessary to see how the science had developed over millennia. During the Palaeolithic period, the Old Stone Age Neanderthals,[15] (our closest ancient human relatives) may have visited Scotland and Ireland whenever climate conditions allowed. We know that they survived for hundreds of years in an environment that people of today would have found extremely challenging, so they must have found ways to medicate themselves. There is evidence of a variety of plants with medicinal properties in a 60,000-year-old Neanderthal grave in Iraq. This could suggest that these 'primitive'

people had equipped the body with healing herbs such as yarrow, ragwort and groundsel, to help prepare them for the journey into the next world.[16] We do not know what they used these herbs for, but at the time the Beatons were practising, all three herbs were used to relieve pain and to treat wounds, swellings and bruises.

In Scotland we can trace the medicinal use of plants back to Neolithic times, as many shrivelled skins of a type of puffball fungus were found at Skara Brae on Orkney. Archaeologists agree that these skins are a rare piece of evidence that point to a herbal treatment. When it gets old, the dried puffball becomes a fibrous material, similar to cotton wool, which helps to stop bleeding and has antiseptic properties, keeping wounds clean.[17] In Perthshire a Bronze Age warrior (*c.*2500 BC to 800 BC) was found with a chest wound packed with sphagnum moss, indicating that the healing properties of that plant also were known.[18] After disappearing from the mainstream medical scene for many years, the antiseptic and absorbent properties of sphagnum moss were 'rediscovered' in the nineteenth century, and later put to good use in both World Wars. Today it is so well-used it even can be bought in bulk online. It is also known that in 2000 BC some surgery was being done – as evidenced by an early Bronze Age trepanned skull found on the Island of Bute.

## Myth, Magic or Medicine: The Druids

The history of medicine shows how societies have changed in their approach to illness and disease over the centuries. People used to believe that ill health had more to do with the supernatural than anything else and many so-called cures belonged to the arena of myth and magic. Inevitably there was an overlap between magical rites and rituals and a variety of medical treatments, as it was not always possible to separate their healing properties into 'real' or 'imagined' categories when dealing with the treatment of the whole person – mind, body and spirit. This approach can be identified in

The Chief Druid (from Thomas Pennant's *A Tour in Wales*, 1781).

the activities of the Druids. Today the word 'Druid' conjures up thoughts of magic, wizardry and spiritualism, but in ancient times the definition of Druid was much broader. During the Iron Age, the Druids made up the higher-educated tier of Celtic society, which included poets, doctors, adjudicators, legal and political advisors and spiritual leaders.[19]

Writing in 1795 for the *First Statistical Account of the Parish of Kilfinichen and Kilvickeon*, Rev. Donald Campbell states that: 'the Druids undoubtedly possessed I [Iona], before the introduction of Christianity . . . The tradition is that the first Christians banished the Druids and took possession of their seat . . . The Druids also had a temple at the head of Lochscridain, in a farm called Rossal. This temple is but small, and several of the stones have fallen down. Here, as the name of the place indicates, they held courts of justice.'[20] There appears to be no other documentary reference to this and certainly there are now no traces of such a building.

The earliest Irish physicians, called '*liaig*' or '*banliaig*' if they were women, were members of this priestly Druid caste.[21] They were greatly skilled in surgery, including trephination and amputations. They also healed with the use of herbs, healing stones, medicated baths, sweat houses and thousands of secret verbal charms, their traditions being handed down orally from remote antiquity. Josina, the 9th

Josina, 9th King of Scotland, by Jacob de Wet, Amsterdam 1697 (Royal Collection, Palace of Holyroodhouse, public domain via Wikimedia Commons).

Detail from 'The Extraction of the Stone of Madness', a painting by Hieronymus Bosch (c.1450-1516) depicting trepanation (Museo del Prada, Madrid, public domain, via Wikimedia Commons).

King of Scots (161 to 37 BC)[22] is supposed to have been educated in Ireland by native physicians and is credited with the authorship of a treatise on the use of herbs.[23]

## Medieval Medicine and Training

The period from the fifth century until the coming of the Normans in the twelfth century was the golden age of ancient Gaelic medicine. Noble families surrounded themselves with entourages of learned men, including physicians, who, like poets, historians and musicians, had high status in Gaelic Ireland, the highest position being *ollaimh leighis*, or official physician to a king, chieftain or Irish lord.

Medicine was the preserve of a select number of families, medical knowledge being passed on to the kinsman most suited to the honour – forming renowned families of hereditary physicians. They were awarded hereditary tenure of land for the medical services they gave; these being passed on to the next generation of the family, in the same fashion. However, the position was no sinecure. The health of a chieftain and his immediate kinsmen would be safeguarded by his personal physician according to strict legal requirements.[24] Under the Irish 'Brehon' laws, thought to be the most advanced system of jurisprudence in the ancient world, were many regulations about medical matters. There were free 'hospitals' (places of safety) for the poor and the sick, whether old, widowed, orphaned, disadvantaged or distressed in other ways, as well as compensation for those who had suffered through medical negligence. There was maintenance for the dependants of the sick or injured during their period of illness, and while physicians were each required to maintain and train four medical students, unqualified physicians were prohibited from practising. The law also dictated that they should be free of debt – and have a plentiful supply of fresh water.

It was within this tradition of Irish hereditary learning that the name of MacBeth or Beaton is first known to be associated with medicine. They owed their allegiance to the Ò Cathan Clan, who owned and occupied land in Ulster during the medieval period. It is likely that there had been a long tradition of medical practice in the family, as the name 'MacBheathadh' means the 'son of life' (*bethe*, 'life').[25] Members of this family were to provide medical services to generations of Irish lords, Scottish kings and chieftains as well as the more common folk. Early members of the clan studied in Aughmacart Medical School. According to William Carrigan, specific details regarding

All that remains of Aughmacart Castle, County Laois, the probable location of the early Medical School. A monastery is said to have been founded here in 550 AD but no vestige of it remains (photo by Kevin Higgins, Creative Commons).

Medieval European Medical Universities visited by Irish Physicians.

the foundation of the school are unavailable, but it was almost certainly long established by 1500.[26] Some of the manuscripts which originated in this school are associated with members of the Beaton kindred. It was also considered important for physicians to have time to study and travel, so that they could become acquainted with new techniques. In the late medieval period, the lack of universities in Ireland encouraged medical students to travel abroad to gain degrees. It was the clans to which they were attached who had the considerable responsibility for financing their training.[27]

It must not be assumed that because Britain and Ireland were islands, their people were isolated from the ideas and culture of the Continent and countries further east. There had been traffic up and down the coasts from time out of mind and traders were not uncommon visitors, bringing news, ideas and information as well as commodities for barter or sale. Thus, the news of the establishment of universities on the Continent and beyond would have filtered through to England, Scotland and especially Ireland. Exactly when the students from various Irish medical kindred began travelling abroad for their education cannot be established, but travel they did and Irish physicians became famed throughout Europe and had connections to the great European medical schools, such as Louvain, Paris, Montpellier, Bologna, Salerno and Padua.

By the second half of the eleventh century, Arabic medicine was being taught at the University of Salerno, and this teaching spread to the rest of Europe by way of other southern universities, particularly Bologna and Montpellier. It was these last two mentioned that were most influential for Irish and Scottish physicians.

The University of Bologna, which was founded in 1088 by an organised guild of students, is the oldest university in continuous operation in the world. It was also the first place of study to use the term 'universitas' for the corporations of students and masters. The Faculty of Medicine there was founded about 1200 and visiting students were accorded significant rights and privileges in return for the revenue they created for the university.

Montpellier's university was founded in 1220 and was one of the great *studia* (or place for study) of Europe. It began as a centre of Roman Catholic learning, but soon came under Jewish and Arabic influences and began to emphasise the secular studies of law and medicines. The medical school was world-renowned during the medieval period, and Guy de Chauliac developed the scientific method

Arnaldus de Villâ Novâ lecturing at the Medica School of Salerno (image from the 1830 publication *Regimen Sanitatis Salernitanum, A Poem on the Preservation of Health in Rhyming Latin Verse*).

Illustration of a herbalist's garden, showing the pattern of small planting beds, from a medieval gardening treatise, described as the first English gardening book, *The Gardener's Labyrinth* by Thomas Hyll, 1577.

of surgery at Montpellier. It is very probable that while the physicians were training in Europe, they would have visited an established physic garden and seen how it was organised, as well as what was being cultivated. Certainly the University of Montpellier had its own Jardin des Plantes as early as 1593. It was created by Pierre Richier de Belleval and is said to have been the oldest in France.

The medical knowledge and expertise of the Irish physicians were mostly based on European ideas, taken from the classical writings of philosophers such as Hippocrates, Aristotle, Galen and the Arab physician Avicenna. The Beatons possessed Gaelic copies of Avicenna's eleventh-century text called *The Book of Healing*, and a version of the *Regimen Sanitatis*, a medieval poem on medical practices involving hygiene and diet (see more about this later).

One of the main functions of the ancient Irish medical schools was the transcription and translation of classical Latin, Greek and Arabic medical texts into Gaelic. These translated manuscripts made available to Irish physicians a wealth of hitherto unknown medical knowledge from the new schools of medicine in Europe. Scholars have concluded that, certainly to begin with, medieval Gaelic medical practice was based on the compilations of Gaelic translations of these classical texts rather than personal observation and experience with patients.[28] As time progressed, though, many of the Gaelic manuscripts were of their own creation and were working documents combining European teaching with Highland and Irish medicine, together with their own traditions and remedies. Later versions were often used as handbooks for diagnosis and treatment, and much of the latter was herbal; these manuscripts were passed down and added to by successive generations. Some of these have survived and are held by repositories in Scotland and England,[29] and will be discussed later in the book.

## Medical Practice and Treatment

The study of the human body was based on the theory of the Four Humours, a theory introduced and expounded by Hippocrates, corresponding to Aristotle's four elements of earth, water, air and fire and their qualities. It was part of a process of combining naturalistic knowledge, philosophy and ancient science to devise a complete understanding of the human body and how it interacts with the world around it.[30] The four humours were: blood/air (warm and moist); yellow bile/fire (warm and dry); black bile/earth (cold and dry); and phlegm/water (cold and moist). So,

each individual might be more or less sanguine, choleric, melancholic or phlegmatic, depending on the combination of humours underlying his or her emotional temperament. The liver produced blood; the brain produced phlegm; the spleen, black bile; and the gallbladder, yellow bile. Illness was caused by an imbalance of these humours, and a diagnosis was made by learning the patient's history and by physical examination. A great variety of foods, plants and animals, as well as minerals and their compounds, were used to treat disease and there are lists (*materia medica*) of nearly 300 medicinal items which could be used.[31] There is also a manuscript containing a list of medicinally useful plants – *Rosa Anglica*[32] – dating from the early fifteenth century.

To maintain balance and ensure good health was the physician's aim, and thus to avoid illness and the necessity for treatment of any sort. The most famous regimen (a systematic plan of diet, therapy and medication) was the *Regimen Sanitatis*, or *Rule of Health*, of which there have been over 100 manuscript and approximately 300 printed editions. One of the copies belonged to John MacBeath (Beaton) of Pennycross, and had remained in the Beaton family for many generations.

This regimen is one of the most popular medical works in history.[33] According to Sir Alexander Croke, the *Regimen* was written for Robert, Duke of Normandy and son of William the Conqueror, who was in Salerno, consulting the physicians there about a

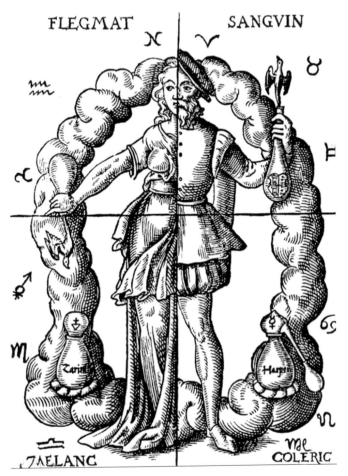

FLEGMAT · SANGVIN

JAELANC · COLERIC

A woodcut depicting the Four Humours by Leonhard Thurneysser in his book *Quinta Essentia*, 1574.

wound which he had received in his right arm from a poisoned arrow and which had degenerated into a sepsis with a local abscess. It was composed as a poem (for easier memorisation) by the physicians of Salerno for the preservation of Robert's health. This fact helps to fix the date of its composition to the end of the eleventh century. The poem was not designed for physicians, but for the general use of an unlearned man, albeit a sovereign's son, and its professed object was the preservation of health rather than the cure of diseases. As such it does not enter into the theory of medicine, but confines itself to a superficial description of the anatomy of the body, stating simply the number of bones, the teeth and

# The *Regimen Sanitatis*

These excerpts from the *Regimen Sanitatis* were translated into English by
Sir John Harington in 1607.

Rise early in the morn', and straight remember
With water cold to wash your hands and eyes,
In gentle fashion stretch every member,
In heat, in cold, in July, and December,
Both comb your head, and rub your teeth likewise.

Garlic then hath power to save from death,
Bear with it though it make unsavoury breath:
And scorn not Garlic like to some, that think
It only makes men wink, and drink and stink.

The Nettles stink, yet make they recompense,
If your belly by the colic pain endures:
Against the colic Nettle-seed and Honey,
Is physic: better none is had for money.
It breedeth sleep, stays vomit, phlegm it doth soften,
It helps him of the gout that eats it often.

Good diet is a perfect way of curing
And worthy much regard and health assuring,
A King that cannot rule him in his diet,
Will hardly rule his Realm in peace and quiet.

But here the Salerne Schoole doth make an end :
And here I cease to write, but will not cease
To wish you live in health, and die in peace :
And ye our Physick rules that friendly read,
God grant that Physick you may never need.

Doctor examining a patient's urine, from a translation of Rhazes (al-Razi) by Gerard of Cremona, c.1250-1260 (reproduced in Samuel Sadaune, *Inventions et Découvertes au Moyen-Âge*, Wikimedia Commons).

the veins. However, it refers in some detail to the four humours and how to preserve health. The work is filled with what is essentially commonsense advice. It is also a source of historical information on the everyday beliefs, thoughts and practices of the Middle Ages; and of authentic contemporary attitudes and prescriptions concerning foodstuffs, such as vegetables, herbs, and meats. There is advice on when to eat, and how much to consume; also what foods were safe and which should be avoided to prevent disease.

When a patient consulted his physician, he would have been examined – an examination which, among other things, would have included the pulse and the urine, this latter study being considered of very great importance. Charts were used showing its colour to help with diagnosis, as the colour reflected the balance of the humours in the body.

Medieval doctors believed that the movements of stars and planets influenced the workings of the human body. They used charts and images to check the positions of the stars to calculate the correct days to carry out procedures and determine when and from which vein blood should be taken.

27

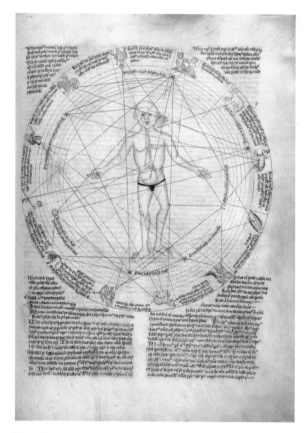

Points for bloodletting, showing the influence of the Zodiac and the planets
(Wellcome Images L0029316, Creative Commons).

The two main ways of taking blood or blood-letting were by the application of leeches, or by venesection, that is removal of blood via a vein. This might also have involved cautery (the burning or sealing of blood vessels) and cupping (holding a warmed glass to the skin, suction increasing the flow of blood). Because it was believed that an excess of blood was the chief cause of disease, its removal appeared to be a logical approach.[34]

Surgery was also employed after injury, including of course, injury in warfare, as the physicians were always in attendance on their lords and responsible for their health at all times. There were other conditions which demanded surgery: for example, 'cutting-for-stone', or 'lithotomy', a dangerous operation to remove a stone from the bladder. There is a record in 1613 of the death of a son of Simon Fraser, 6th Lord Lovat, having been cut-for-stone by the

A page from one of the manuscripts in the Beaton Library, with additional notes by the Beaton Physicians. The calendar of the lunar cycle has been recognised as that of the year 1538. The heading on this page reads, 'On determining the dominical letter and golden number'. Underneath are drawn the circular devices used to find this letter, which tells which day is Sunday, and the 'golden number', which helps find the date of Easter, the most important feast in the Church's calendar. Later on in the text are notes on diet and other aspects of health relating to the month in question (National Library of Scotland, Adv. MS 72.1.33.f.1.v.).

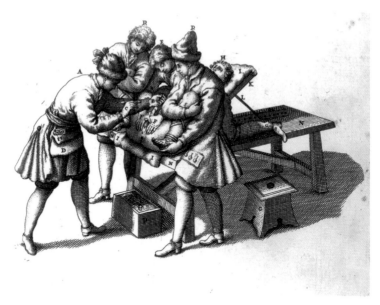

'The Lithotomy Position' (from Tommaso Alghisi, *Litotomia*, Florence, 1707). (Wellcome Images L0015225, Creative Commons).

Fraser physician, Gill-eandris Beatton.[35] Yet another Beaton, Neil of Skye, in the late seventeenth century, had 'the boldness to cut a piece of a woman's skull broader than a half a crown', in order to relieve her headaches.[36]

## Changing Ways

Inevitably, with the passage of time, the old ways of approaching disease changed, as did its treatment. Each era brings its great medical practitioners who make unique advances in the understanding of medicine and surgery. The invention of printing meant that medical textbooks, with accurate sketches of the human body, could now be produced more cheaply, increasing anatomical knowledge and helping the new ideas to spread more rapidly. No longer were the treasured manuscripts of such importance to the medical practitioners of the Renaissance.

Scottish universities also underwent changes and their revitalisation was finally producing a quality of education which could equal that offered in Europe.[37]

These changes came too late for the Beatons of Pennycross, who flourished during the later years of the medieval period. By the time the new ideas of the Renaissance penetrated the Highlands and Islands of Scotland, the Beatons (as will be seen) had lost their power and position. However, their reputation was such that tales of their skill and sagacity remained for generations and the remaining manuscripts they so carefully preserved are now items of wonder, interest and admiration.

Two parallel medicinal traditions emerged from the period sometimes known as the Dark Ages: male physicians were monastic or university-trained and attended to the rich and powerful, whilst folk healers, usually women, based their treatment on plant remedies and tended to serve the poorer levels of society, often living in rural areas. It would seem that the Beatons managed to combine these two traditions, having a profound knowledge of the classical principles and a good understanding of the properties of the plants growing around them. They would surely have found it necessary to establish designated areas for the cultivation of those plants which formed the basis of their herbal pharmacopeia.

# 2

# *Discovering the Pennycross Physicians*

## The Four Principal Physicians to the Macleans of Duart

### Andrew Beaton and the Land at Pennycross

Following the forfeiture of power of the Lords of the Isles in 1493, the Beatons retained their connection with the Macleans of Duart and became increasingly well-known in the Isle of Mull. However, it was not until nearly one hundred years later that the farm of Pennycross became associated with the kindred. It was on 20 October 1572 that a writ was signed by Hector Maclean, 9th Laird of Duart, granting land at Pennycross in Brolas, Mull to: 'Andrew MacDonel vik inoldif his servant . . . together with the supreme and principall office of surgeon within all the territories currently in the possession of the MacLeans of Duart'.[38] It was also stated that male heirs 'sufficiently Instructed and Qualified for exercising the medicinal Art,' should retain the 'Lands of Pennycross lying in Broloss Island of Mull

for payment of the yearly feu duties of half a mart[39] 3st[one] oatmeal, 2st[one] Cheese & 1 Boll of Malt upon the grounds of the Sands of Broloss or Kilfinichen wherever they should be required for that effect'.[40]

The land awarded to Andrew Mak in olliff (Andrew the Physician) by Maclean of Duart in 1572 was not an estate, but a farm, which lay – and still lies – between Pennyghael and Killunaig, two other farms belonging to Maclean. It was not a particularly large farm, as can be seen from an estate map of 1819, as the marches or boundaries would not have changed in the intervening centuries. Why Maclean chose this farm is not recorded; it may be that when the time came for a gift to be made to Andrew, the chief looked around at all his holdings and found that the most convenient one at the time, for whatever reason, was Pennycross. In 1572 it was probably not a multi-tenanted farm, as, although the

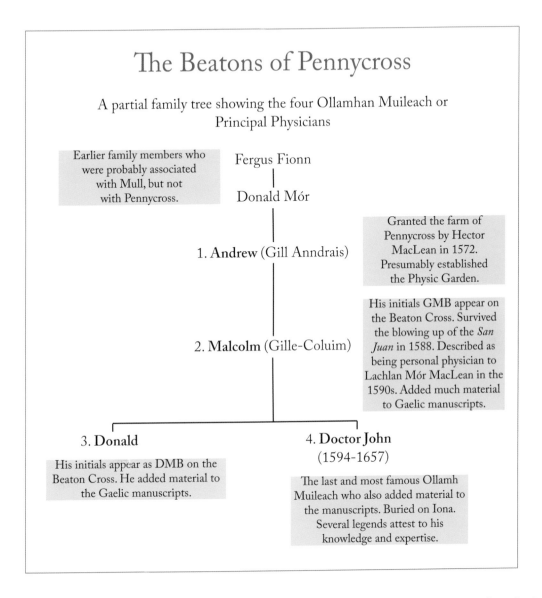

# The Beatons of Pennycross

A partial family tree showing the four Ollamhan Muileach or
Principal Physicians

Earlier family members who
were probably associated
with Mull, but not
with Pennycross.

Fergus Fionn

Donald Mór

1. **Andrew** (Gill Anndrais)

Granted the farm of
Pennycross by Hector
MacLean in 1572.
Presumably established
the Physic Garden.

2. **Malcolm** (Gille-Coluim)

His initials GMB appear on
the Beaton Cross. Survived
the blowing up of the *San
Juan* in 1588. Described as
being personal physician to
Lachlan Mór MacLean in the
1590s. Added much material
to Gaelic manuscripts.

3. **Donald**

His initials appear as DMB on the
Beaton Cross. He added material to
the Gaelic manuscripts.

4. **Doctor John**
(1594-1657)

The last and most famous Ollamh
Muileach who also added material to
the manuscripts. Buried on Iona.
Several legends attest to his
knowledge and expertise.

small tenants had no leases or security of tenure, it would have been troublesome to turn out several tenants and their families, at a time when the clan system was still strong. So it is possible to conjecture that the farm had formerly been occupied by a single small tenant, perhaps a relation of the chief himself, or of the tacksman of the time.

If this had happened back in the twelfth or thirteenth centuries, according to the Brehon Law, this would not have been an unusual occurrence and one with which the Beatons would have been familiar. However, time had moved on, and the Beaton physicians had been practising on the island and serving the Macleans for well over 100 years before this land grant. So perhaps there was a specific incident, a special cure involving Hector Maclean that precipitated the action. The fact that there are at least two legends explaining the Beaton acquisition may strengthen this theory. However, they are strangely at odds with each other.

The first story was told to Thomas Scott Muir by Miss Maclean of Pennycross in 1856 and, briefly, runs like this: 'MacLean of Duart was wounded by a poisoned arrow, and his case thought hopeless: Beaton, to the wonder of the world, established a cure, for which the laird presented him with Pennycross in perpetuity.'[41] Sadly, the second legend puts Beaton in a far less favourable light as it intimates that the Doctor was responsible for the death of MacGillivray of Glencannel. These tales are told in more detail later in the book. However it happened, and whatever the real facts were, a family of the Beaton medical kindred was established on the farm of Pennycross in Brolas, an association with the area which lasted for nearly two hundred years.

We know little more about this first inhabitant of Pennycross, except that his name – Andrew Mak in olliff – appears as a witness

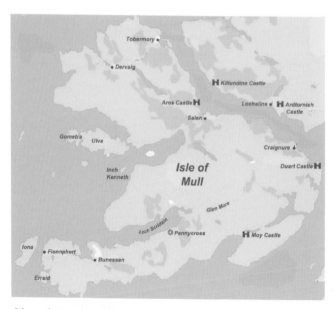

Map of the Isle of Mull, showing the position of Pennycross.

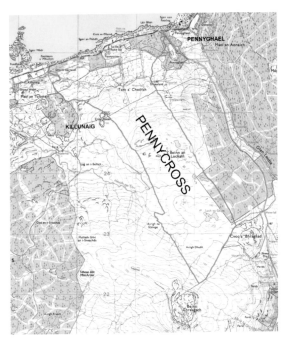

Map of Pennycross land, showing the boundaries with Killunaig Farm to the west and Pennyghael Farm to the east.

to another charter by Hector Maclean on 1 January 1574.[42] However, we can surmise that it was during Andrew's tenure at Pennycross that a house was built and a physic garden established, where he could cultivate the medicinal plants he required. The same Miss Maclean who told Muir of the legend concerning the acquisition of the land, is also reported as saying: 'It is but lately the house they dwelt in at Pennycross was pulled down, though the garden still exists, and contains many medicinal shrubs, which the country people think have a peculiar virtue, and use them for their children's ailments, I believe.'[43]

When Andrew Beaton arrived with his family, it is probable that the news had spread through the district that a distinguished physician was moving into the area. But although the family members would have been of higher status than most of the local residents they would still have lived in very similar conditions. The house in which the family lived would have looked like others in the neighbourhood, though it was probably stone-built from the start – and not constructed from turf. It may also have had a stone floor. However, to a 'foreign' visitor, it would have appeared quite primitive. Dr Samuel Johnson in his *Journey to the Western Islands* described his visit with Boswell to Sir Allan Maclean, 'the chieftain of the great clan of Maclean', on Inch Kenneth in 1773. They 'found one cottage for Sir Allan, and I think two more for domesticks and the offices, occupied not by a gross herdsman, or amphibious fisherman, but by a gentleman and two ladies, of high birth, polished manners and elegant conversation . . . in a habitation raised not very far above the ground, but furnished with unexpected neatness and convenience.'[44]

Island dwellings were of a simple, traditional design, indigenous to the area, and reflected the social life of the community and the manners and customs of their way of life. They were not places of luxury; their primary function was to give shelter from cold, wind and rain, while providing for simple social activities around the peat fire. Early houses in this area had all four walls of the same height with roofs of hip-end construction. Uniquely, on Mull, there was a composite design, in which a gable was built at one end of the house and at

Part of an estate plan, surveyed in 1817 by Alexander Langlands for Alexander, 3rd Maclean of Pennycross, whose estate at that time comprised the farms of Carvolg, Carsaig, Kinloch, Aird, Leidle, Pennyghael, Pennycross, Killunaig and Torrans. The map shows the worked fields. (Reproduced with permission from the Glaisher family.)

A traditional-style house on the Ross of Mull, with the unique 'Mull roof' (sketch by Jackie Le May, courtesy of Mark Le May).

The interior of a house with the unique Mull design of hanging chimney set against the gable. Although this painting was done over a hundred years after the Beatons had left their farm at Pennycross, it is likely that the basic design of the house would have changed very little (painting by Iona McVean, courtesy of Colin Houston).

# An t-Ollamh, the Mull Doctor

(pronounced ant o-luv)

The Gaelic word *Ollamh* originally meant the highest grade of poet but came to mean a master in any profession or craft.

By the middle of the sixteenth century in Scotland, the term had become associated particularly with medicine, so the term '*Mac an ollamh*' meant 'son of the physician'. Thus the title *An t-Ollamh Muileach* – The Ollamh of Mull – was understood to refer to a medical man without any further explanation. It was universally understood that the skill required to hold the position of *An t-Ollamh Muileach* – the Mull Doctor – was that of medicine, not of any other profession or craft.

the other, the sides of the roof sloped downwards to the walls, forming a 'hip-end'. A timber frame formed a 'couple roof', the simplest form of pitched roof, in which the 'couples', two rafters, sloped upwards from the opposite walls and met on a ridge piece or 'purlin', a horizontal beam running down the middle of the roof. The walls were of stone and turf, the floors of beaten earth and the roofs thatched. The thatch, probably formed of rushes in this area, was laid on a bedwork of sods and held down with straw ropes, hazel twigs acting as pins and binding hoops. The smallest houses had only one room; others had an integral byre and perhaps a small room off the kitchen. In the 'Mull' design of house, a hanging chimney of wood was set against the gable, with a projecting stone hob, and an iron bracket or 'swee'

for the pot chain and a timber hood or canopy. In other houses the peat fire was central. Sanitation was completely absent and water was carried by hand from a neighbouring well or burn.[45]

Although the interior plan of the house would have been similar to others on the island, there would presumably have been no integral byre and the social status and medical interests of each succeeding Beaton would probably have meant that there were items in the house which were foreign to those of his neighbours. Also, it is likely that members of the family would have dressed in a less primitive manner. The basic style of dress would probably have remained similar, but they would have been able to purchase good material for their clothes and employ people to make them. They may well have received such goods in lieu of cash payments or as gifts. The Beaton family would have had several servants: some indoor servants and some to work the farm and help tend the physic garden. It is unlikely that the principal surgeon, An t-Ollamh Muileach himself, would have been involved in farm work, though it is more than likely that he would have overseen the medicinal plants in the physic garden. Over the years, the Beatons rented out parts of the farm; it is known that, latterly, they were living off the rents of their farm.

Due to a lack of documentary evidence, however, most of these details are a matter for conjecture.

## The Beatons' Physic Garden

What would the garden at Pennycross have looked like in the days when the four Ollaimh Muileach were in residence? While it would not be sensible to imagine a formal structure on a grand scale at Pennycross, it is likely that there would have been planning in the construction and maintenance of a functioning

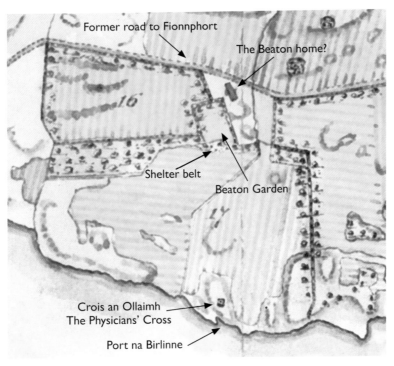

A close up of the area assumed to be the Beaton Physic Garden on Pennycross Farm and a possible house site (taken from the Langlands Estate map of 1817).

Thomas Hyll's illustration of planting, from his book *The Gardener's Labyrinth*.

physic garden if it were to produce useful plants. As many of the plants the physicians had encountered on the continent would have been impossible to grow on a Hebridean island, they would have needed the advice and knowledge of local experts. These were most likely to have been the local Wise Women, whose herbal knowledge had been handed down for generations.

When Isabel MacEachainn, a cottar from Bunessan, was interviewed by Alexander Carmichael for his *Carmina Gadelica*,[46] she recounted several poems and anecdotes about the plants she remembered being used, including this one:

The Pearlwort
(Latin: *sagina procumbens*. Gaelic: *mòthan*.)

I will cull the Pearlwort
Beneath the fair sun of Sunday,
Beneath the gentle hand of the Virgin,
She who will defend me,
In the might of the Trinity
Who granted it to grow.

Isabel also told Carmichael that a cow which ate pearlwort is sained (blessed) and no evil influence could affect her, the calf she carried, the milk she gave or the man, woman or child who drank that milk.

The mòthan or mòlus (pearlwort, bog violet or butterwort) is rare, and is found in Mull on the moorland and the hill. It has five- or six-pointed leaves and red roots. It is a *lus beannaichte* (blessed plant) according to some, because it was the first plant on which Christ placed his foot after he rose from the dead. It was supposed to have many attributes:

> If placed over the *àrd doras* (lintel of the door) it prevents the *slugagh* (airy host) from entering the house and spiriting away any of the household.
>
> When placed under the right knee of a woman in labour, it has a soothing spiritual effect on the woman, ensures her relief, and secures to her and her child immunity from being spirited away by fairies.
>
> It is used in many districts for a love-philtre. If a girl be kissed by her lover while even a small piece of the mòthan is in her mouth, the lover is ever after her adoring slave.

Many of these stories would have been heard by the physicians, some indeed ending up in a manuscript, perhaps indicating that the doctor had found the cure successful.

In all the old illustrations of physic or herbal gardens, the land is divided into small

Pounding herbs to release their essential oils, from the *Hortus Sanitatis* c.1497, reproduced in *The Gardener's Labyrinth*.

beds. We don't know how the Beatons would have organised their plots, but it is likely that they followed the tradition of planting according to usage – those used for different ailments: digestive problems, respiratory conditions, injuries, wounds and so on. It would also have been necessary to separate out those which were dangerous – poisonous in certain circumstances. A good many plants are efficacious when applied externally but can kill if taken internally. It is likely that these plants would have been grown at some distance from other more benign herbs and perhaps fenced off, to keep children and animals away from unintentional harm. It is interesting to note that, well into the twentieth century, children were being warned not to touch any plants in the area known to have been part of the old Beaton garden.[47]

The physicians would have known which plants could be grown in the shade and which needed a lot of light; those that needed well-drained soil and those that could withstand the wet; those that needed the shelter of a dyke, trees or larger plants, and those that could stand up to the Hebridean storms.[48] They would certainly have needed to memorise what was growing where, in case plants had to be plucked in the dark, or during the drear wet weather when visibility is poor.

Some plants were used fresh, others would have been picked in season, dried and stored; some reduced to powder, some mixed and made into lotions, pastes or poultices. Seeds would also have been collected and they would all have needed to be stored somewhere safe and dry, possibly in a room in the physician's house.

It seems sensible to suggest that whenever the physician was called to visit another part of the island, a patient on the mainland or in Ireland, he would have taken with him a selection of local plants in one form or another. These may well have been for his own use but could also have been for exchange with fellow physicians from other parts of the country, who were growing plants unavailable at Pennycross.

As the land at Pennycross is on basalt, there would have been plants that would simply not have thrived there, and it is reasonable to assume that other herb gardens were established in various parts of the island where there is a different soil structure. There is a local story that such a garden existed somewhere near Scoor on the Ross of Mull, where the rock is granite, though it has never been possible to identify it. There were Beaton physicians at Dervaig, where again the growing conditions are different, so it is likely that the doctors worked together to obtain the maximum number of different plants to treat their patients.

## Malcolm Beaton and the Tobermory Galleon

Malcolm's birth and death dates are unknown, but there is evidence he was living and working between 1582 and 1603.

Malcolm was Andrew's son and assumed his title of An t-Ollamh Muileach sometime

A ship on the high seas caught by a squall. Painting 'The Gust' by Willem van de Velde the Younger (c.1680), Rijksmuseum, Amsterdam (in public domain).

before 1582, when he acted as witness to a precept of sasine in a charter by Sir Lachlan Mór Maclean of Duart.[49] Proof that Malcolm was indeed successor to his father as principal physician comes in a Gaelic letter written to him between 1593 and 1596 by Sir Lachlan, in which Malcolm is addressed as Sir Lachlan's 'personal physician', when being commanded to attend his sister Marion in Ardgour and visit his cousin in Appin.[50]

By the time Malcolm was principal physician, the fact of the Beaton residency at Pennycross was well-established and widely known, not just on Mull, but much further afield. His initials G. M. B. (Gille-Coluim MacBheathadh), appear on a wayside cross,

overlooking Loch Scridain, together with those of his son and the date of 1582. The cross was probably set up as a waymarker or sign to travellers that they had arrived at the doctor's dwelling. The cross is described later in this chapter.

In 1588 Malcolm Beaton was involved in a famous incident on board a Spanish vessel in Tobermory Bay. Formerly identified as the *Florencia*, and usually called *San Juan de Sicilia* or *San Juan* for short, it was part of the Spanish Armada.[51] 'Driven by tempest to the west part of Scotland to the Isle caulled Mula in MacLanes countrie',[52] the *San Juan* was severely damaged and Sir Lachlan Mór Maclean of Duart granted to the ship stores

The cover of the medical manuscript to which Donald contributed (National Library of Scotland Adv. MS 72.1.33). The document was bound with thread into a leather cover, large enough to provide flaps all round the manuscript, and had a rough sheepskin clasp.

and other assistance in exchange for the use of a company of the troops on board to assist him in besieging Mingary Castle. This attempt proved unsuccessful but the troops also helped carry out other local acts of attack and plunder. Beaton would have been present as Maclean's personal physician at all his military enterprises, helping to deal with injuries to the common soldiers as well as to the Chief.

However, while moored in Tobermory Bay, the ship was apparently sabotaged. It is still not known for sure who instigated this, possibly Sir Lachlan Mór, possibly even Elizabeth I of England. Whoever was responsible, the ship was blown up and as a result, it burned and sank. Only a few people were saved. In 1589 an official report of the 'accident' was sent to the Privy Council, in which it was stated how many men had been lost 'saving twoe or three that were blowen on the shoaare with the upper decke, so that nothing was saved that was in her at that instant, and what remained unburned is nowe sunke under water'.[53] It would seem that one of the fortunate people blown clear in this explosion was An t-Ollamh Muileach himself – Malcolm Beaton. Martin Martin, the great traveller and Gaelic speaker from Skye, who produced a first-hand account of the society and natural history of Scotland in around 1695, wrote of this event: 'Several of the inhabitants of Mull told me that they had conversed with their relations that were living at the harbour when this ship was blown up; and they gave an account of an admirable providence that appeared in the preservation of one Dr Beaton (the famous physician of Mull), who was on board the ship when she blew up, and was then sitting on the upper deck, which was blown up entire, and thrown a good way off; yet the doctor was saved; and lived several years after.'[54]

Malcolm has also been described as an industrious contributor to the growing collection of Gaelic medical manuscripts, physicians'

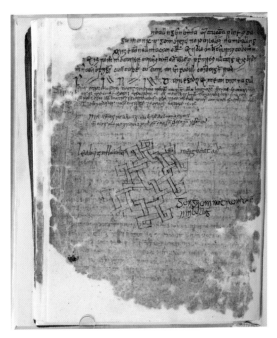

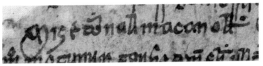

Above: at the end of the manuscript is a colophon (a statement at the end of a book or manuscript giving facts about its production). Below: Donald has signed his name as being involved in the compilation of the treatise; it appears as Domhnall mac an ollaimh (Donald, son of the physician).

textbooks and Vade Mecum handbooks or guides, which were kept constantly at hand for consultation. Only a small proportion of the Beaton collection still remains, 25 manuscripts in all, but many of those that have survived show signs of Malcolm's work. (See the chapter on the Beaton Library.)

## Donald and the Crois an Ollaimh

Donald's birth and death dates are also unknown, but it is clear that he was already fully qualified and practising as a physician in 1582, because his initials D. M. B. appear on the Crois an Ollaimh (the Physicians' Cross) with those of his father G. M. B. (see below). He was Malcolm Beaton's eldest son and succeeded him as the third Ollamh Muileach sometime before 1603.[55] It is also likely that he didn't survive long after his father's death. We know little of Donald's life, although it is clear that he spent some time in Donegal, Ireland, as his distinctive handwriting has shown researchers that he was involved in adding material to an existing Gaelic medical treatise.[56]

On his return to Mull, Donald would have given the extended manuscript back to his father Malcolm, who had already added his own contribution to the work.

It was during the lifetime of Malcolm and Donald, father and son, that their initials appeared on what has become known as The Beaton Cross. This is a roughly hewn Latin cross in Moine granulite, possibly made sometime between 700 and 800 AD. It is similar to many other medieval crosses of the period and may

The Beaton Cross (photo by Miek Zwamborn).

A visiting boat arriving at Port na Birlinne (sketch by Graham Kent).

The Beaton Cross, photographed by Flora McVean on 17 January 1899, showing the stepped drystone base. The brand-new Free Church can be seen in the background. (Reproduced by courtesy of Colin Houston.)

## Tracks and Drove Roads through Glen More, Isle of Mull

As the Beaton physicians were known to be part of the entourage of the Lords of the Isles from the 1300s, they would have been very familiar with the birlinn, whether for normal travel or for warfare.

Two centuries later, in the 1570s, the decade in which Andrew (Gill-An-ndrais) Beaton arrived at Pennycross, travel overland was still difficult and dangerous. Most of the population seldom travelled any distance at all – just to neighbouring townships. Those with occupations which demanded a certain amount of movement on land used the tracks and drove roads that criss-crossed the hills, linking settlements and coastal ports. The greatest mileage done on land was probably undertaken by the drovers, who would drive their beasts from all over the island to Achnacraig (Grasspoint, Isle of Mull), from whence they took to the water.

At least one of the main thoroughfares that we take for granted today did not exist in the sixteenth century – the road through the Great Glen, Glen More. As can be seen from the map, the area was well supplied with tracks and drove roads, which crossed the Mams (the passes over the mountains) and gave access to the townships; but even in later centuries, visiting explorers and writers were deploring the difficulties of travelling by road on Mull. As late as 1818, Keats wrote, 'the road through the island, or rather the track, is the most dreary you can think of – between dreary mountains – over bog and rock and river with our Breeches tucked up and our Stockings in hand'.

have been an early example of recycling, as it is thought that it was erected at Pennycross many centuries later.[57]

On the east face of the shaft are carved the initials G. M. B. and D. M. B. in Roman capitals, with the date 1582 written between them. It is believed that the initials stand for Gille-Coluim (Malcolm) MacBheathadh and his son Domhnall (Donald). Members of the Beaton family before the seventeenth century used the surnames MacBheathadh and Mac an Ollaimh indiscriminately. The initials were seen and spoken of into the nineteenth century, but during the twentieth, they have gradually become almost invisible under the increasing encrustation of lichen. Current opinion accepts the fact that climate change is the main factor in this increase, and also that the lichen should not be removed for fear of doing more damage to the stonework.[58] In addition to this, discerning the physicians' initials is made more difficult by the existence of odd bits of graffiti.

Travel by water was the norm during the early centuries in this part of the world. In fact, this remained the case until (relatively) good roads were established in the nineteenth century. Tracks overland were often washed away in bad weather, and even in good weather they presented difficulties. Travellers coming from afar invariably came by water. Important visitors and those travelling any distance would have come by birlinn, the medieval galley, and they would have been able to moor their vessels in Port na Birlinne, a small cove just to the east of the cross site. Thus it is likely that the cross was set up where it is as a waymarker to vessels coming into Loch Scridain from

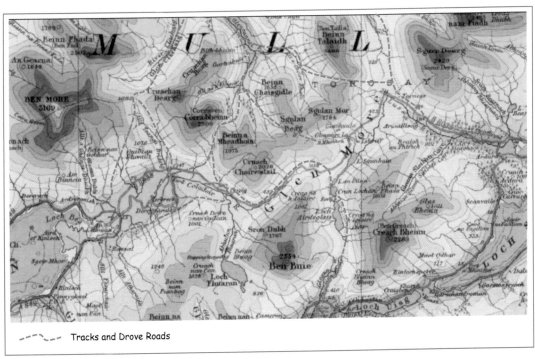

Tracks and Drove Roads

The tracks and drove roads through Glen More, Isle of Mull (map base reproduced by permission of the National Library of Scotland).

The Beaton Cross within the protective railings erected to prevent more graffiti
(photo by Miek Zwamborn).

the open sea. It is only in recent years that the surrounding land has been shrouded in vegetation. From Port na Birlinne, it is only a few hundred yards inland to the Physic Garden and supposed site of the Beaton house.

Although at present the cross is only 1.28m in height, originally it was probably taller, as the shaft extends for a further 0.57m into the stepped drystone base and is broken off at the bottom. This may be the reason for the construction of the pedestal. There is a possibility that when the cross was first placed in its position at Pennycross, it stood proud, with no stone surround. Most of the crosses erected in earlier centuries stood alone, so the theory that the base was added following the breaking of the shaft is quite plausible. What we do

know is that when the cross was described in 1861, the base was already in place. 'At Pennycross there is rather an interesting wayside object, namely, a cruciform pillar about four and a half feet in height, elevated on a pedestal of several steps.'[59]

About a century later, after it was observed that graffiti was appearing on one face of the shaft, railings were erected around the cross by Brigadier Alasdair Maclean of Pennycross. In 2018, it was recognised that some of the stones in the dry-stone base had shifted, and in 2019, consolidation and repair work was undertaken under the auspices of Adopt-a-Monument, an Archaeology Scotland initiative funded by Historical Environment Scotland.

## Dr John Beaton, the Illustrious Physician

John Beaton was the fourth and last Ollamh Muileach of Pennycross and seems to have been considered the most illustrious. He was commonly referred to as Doctor John. It is known that John had succeeded to his title by 1633, as there exist two bonds by Sir Lachlan Maclean, 17th Clan Chief, dated that year and signed in Latin by John Beaton as his servitor.[60] His name also appears next to additions to one of the manuscripts in the Beaton Library, in which he gave his date of birth as 1594.[61] Later, in 1651, in the Minutes of the Synod of Argyll, he is referred to as 'John Beaton, physician, living within the parish of Kilvickewan.'[62]

John married twice. His first marriage produced one son, Neil, who will feature later. From his second marriage, there were at least three sons. None of these men took over as physician to the Macleans. This was not just because of the type of succession practised within the kindred; it was also because of the political situation of the time. According to writings of 1702, John was probably the last to fill the office of principal physician. Nineteenth-century tradition also records that he was 'the last of the eminent race of the physicians' and indicates that he had no successor as physician to the Macleans of Duart.[63] As with the other Ollamh Muileach, John added to the manuscript library over the years and his name appears frequently.

John is buried in Iona. His grave slab, which was not erected until some years later, was formerly in Reilig Òdhrain, (St Oran's Graveyard) and can now be seen in the cloisters of Iona Abbey. The grave slab is described later in this chapter.

We know just as little about the life of John as we do of the earlier three chief physicians. However, as has been mentioned, it is often said that he was the most distinguished of the Pennycross medical men. Thus the well-known legend concerning Doctor John's death is not so surprising, as it illustrates the jealousy of other physicians towards a rival who was held in high regard by the greatest in the land. This tale however, throws up some historical difficulties, if it really does refer to Doctor John Beaton. We know the date of his death as 1657 and at this date, there was no king on the Scottish throne, as Oliver Cromwell was still Lord Protector of England, Scotland, and Ireland (1653-1658). The following version of the story comes from John McCormick, *The Island of Mull*, pp. 126-127.

The manner in which Doctor John Beaton, Ollamh Muileach, met his death, was tragic. It is recorded that the then King of Scotland, wishing to determine who was the most able physician in his realm, feigned an illness. He summoned 25 of the most noted physicians to make a diagnosis of his complaint. Among those summoned was Doctor Beaton. When local people knew that he was to leave immediately for Edinburgh, they gathered round and asked advice as to

Above, a page from the sixteenth to seventeenth-century medical compendium assembled by several Mull Beatons, often known as 'The Beaton Manuscript'. In the upper margin Doctor John Beaton (1594-1657) has signed himself: 'leabar Eoin mhic Mhic Bethadh' (National Library of Scotland Adv. MS 72.1.2, f. 124 r). Below, a close-up of Doctor John's signature.

their health during his absence. Beaton advised them, 'Be cheerful, temperate and early risers.' He then made his departure. When he arrived at the court, he found a strange situation. Neither he nor any of the other physicians was allowed to make an examination of the King – tradition says that they were not even allowed to enter his room. Beaton soon realised that the King was playing a trick on them, and because of his wise judgement was received into the royal favour. However, he was not to enjoy this for long. As may be imagined, the situation caused a good deal of jealousy on the part of the other physicians, and they conspired together to destroy him. On their way back from the Royal Palace, they bribed the keeper of the first stage-house to help carry out their plot. Beaton and his ghillie arrived at the stage-house a short time after the others had left, and being tired, decided to stop and rest for a while. Doctor John asked for a drink of water, which he was given. He drank it down and the moment he did so, pressed his hands to his breast in pain. He immediately asked the landlord for milk. The man replied that there was none in the house. So Beaton then asked his servant to go out into the kailyard and quickly bring some cabbage. The servant rushed off, but when he returned he had to tell Beaton that there was not a stick of cabbage left in the ground – it had all been removed. Beaton by this time was suffering badly from the poison which had been

administered in the water. He said to his servant, 'Take care of yourself, and get home in safety, I am poisoned.' In a few moments, he breathed his last. The trap had been well prepared. The villains who laid it took care that any emetic, such as milk or cabbage, would be put beyond his reach.

'So ended, it is said, the life of a man whose name is still green in his native land.'

## The End of an Era, the Demise of the Ollamh Muileach

The political situation which developed during John's lifetime has already been mentioned and needs some explanation. During the sixteenth century successive heads of the Duart Macleans took a prominent part in the perpetual feuds with which the Western Isles were afflicted, and several marriages with the Campbells brought them into close, though not always friendly, relations with the House of Argyll.[64] However, during the Civil War of the seventeenth century their fortunes began to decline, and the century saw an exacerbation of the developing feud between the houses of Duart and Argyll.

Briefly, the Marquis of Argyll held both the feudal superiority over Duart and a mortgage on the estate and had been trying to foreclose for some years. There could never be peace and accord between the two families. The Macleans were of the traditional clan heritage, where a man's word was his bond;

# When and Why Did the Farm of Pennycross Acquire Its Name?

Is it too obvious to assume it was because of the existence of the stone cross erected there?

Back in the mists of time, when an area became settled, it would quickly become essential to identify it, so it can be assumed that placenames were adopted many centuries ago. Some names, however, would change over time; for example, when the Vikings and Norse settlers were colonising parts of Scotland from the eighth century onwards, some pre-existing Norse names were obliterated. Many names on Mull are from the Gaelic language, and gradually became anglicised once maps and other documentation came into existence.

The name Pennycross means the Pennyland of the Cross. A pennyland was a measure of value, not of area. It was so called because the 'scat' or tax paid on it was a pennyweight of silver. This method of assessing land values goes back to the Norse occupation of the Western Isles (*c*.900-1266 AD) as the word was originally Norse, not Gaelic. Thus it would appear that a number of farms in Mull, such as Pennycross and Pennyghael, had their boundaries fixed during the time when the Norsemen ruled in the Western Isles and called their homesteads names like Rossal (Horse field) and Burg (Fort).

According to Anglo-Saxon historians and other specialists, the cross standing on Pennycross land is likely to have been made sometime around 700 or 800 AD; no-one is prepared to be more precise. But does this mean the Vikings erected it here? This seems unlikely, as it was the Vikings who sacked the religious sites on Iona, beginning in 795 AD and continuing to 825 AD. The Book of Settlements (Landnámabók) does record traditions that some Norse Hebrideans had adopted Christianity by the 870s, but even if this were the case in Mull, why would relatively few Viking settlers erect a cross in this place?

In many documentary records, it is assumed that the Cross was set up in 1582, at a time when Gille-Coluim (Malcolm) MacBethadh and his son Domhnall (Donald) MacBethadh were practising physicians at Pennycross. As has been mentioned, it would have been placed in this strategic position, immediately next to Port na Birlinn, to act as a signpost for visitors arriving by sea to the house of the Ollamh Muileach. The alternative scenario is that an existing cross on this site had the initials carved on its shaft in 1582.

However, if this Cross was not set up until 1582, why had the land been called Pennycross for the previous thousand years . . . (give or take)?

the Campbells were of the modern mould, whereby a man's signature on a legal document would win the day. Each side has its own version of the whole affair, which amounted at times to a private war, but one which caused misery and destitution to many.[65]

The Maclean cause was not helped by the premature deaths of several of their chieftains, who were succeeded each time by minors. In 1651, Sir Hector Maclean, 18th Chief of Duart, was killed at the Battle of Inverkeithing, and succeeded by his brother Sir Allan, at that time only four years of age. Sir Allan, 19th Clan Chief of Duart, died at the age of only twenty-seven, when Lachlan Maclean of Brolas undertook the management of the affairs of the estate on behalf of Sir Allan's infant son, John. The outcome of this turbulent time was probably inevitable – the Campbells gained control of Duart and most of the Maclean estates by 1679. With the disintegration of the court and household of Duart, and the general disruption of the whole island, it is little wonder that the position of Official Physician to the Chief was discontinued.

## The Last of the Medical Kindred of Pennycross

### Fergus Beaton, Inhabitant of Pennycross

When John Beaton died in 1657, the succession reverted back to Fergus, son of his elder brother Donald. Fergus's birth and death dates are unknown, but we know he was living and working between 1657 and 1674 as his signature appears on various manuscripts.

As has been explained, there was now no official position of Principal Physician to hand on. However, Fergus did inherit three things: a medical training, the lands of Pennycross and the priceless Beaton collection of manuscripts.

It would seem that although Fergus Beaton was still practising medicine, it was in reduced circumstances, and he is described simply as an inhabitant of Pennycross. Alongside a Beaton pedigree in one of the manuscripts is written: '*Hic Liber est Fergusii McVeagh, habitantis Peanagross*',[66] meaning, 'this book belongs to Fergus McBeth, who lives at Pennycross'.

Following Fergus's death around 1674, the succession once again moved sideways, as his son Malcolm, who will appear later, was possibly not even a physician. However, it appears that Fergus's wife continued to live at Pennycross, and to 'enjoy the life rent' until her death in 1718 – another 44 years.[67]

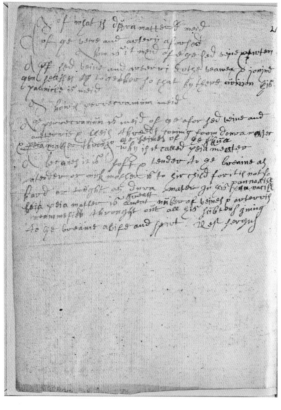

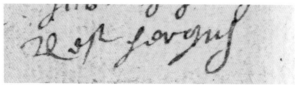

Above, another page from the medical compendium by the Mull Beatons, on which are a series of student's notes in English, taking the form of questions and answers on the anatomy of the pericranium. Below, at the end of the page, Fergus signed his name (National Library of Scotland Adv. MS 72.1.2, f.27v).

# The Beatons of Pennycross

Continuation of the family tree. The Beatons no longer held official positions with the MacLeans of Duart, but were still associated with the lands of Pennycross.

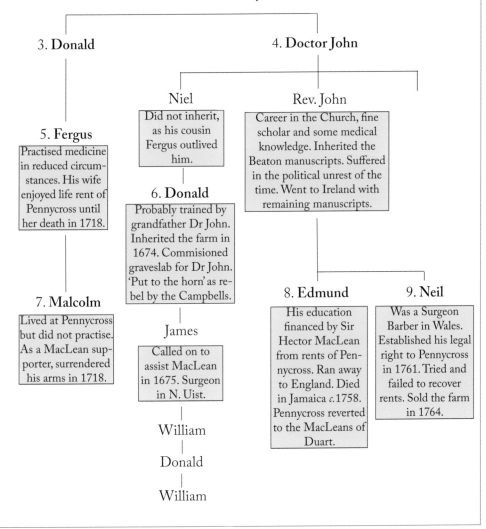

**3. Donald**

**4. Doctor John**

Niel
Did not inherit, as his cousin Fergus outlived him.

Rev. John
Career in the Church, fine scholar and some medical knowledge. Inherited the Beaton manuscripts. Suffered in the political unrest of the time. Went to Ireland with remaining manuscripts.

**5. Fergus**
Practised medicine in reduced circumstances. His wife enjoyed life rent of Pennycross until her death in 1718.

**6. Donald**
Probably trained by grandfather Dr John. Inherited the farm in 1674. Commisioned graveslab for Dr John. 'Put to the horn' as rebel by the Campbells.

**7. Malcolm**
Lived at Pennycross but did not practise. As a MacLean supporter, surrendered his arms in 1718.

James
Called on to assist MacLean in 1675. Surgeon in N. Uist.

**8. Edmund**
His education financed by Sir Hector MacLean from rents of Pennycross. Ran away to England. Died in Jamaica c.1758. Pennycross reverted to the MacLeans of Duart.

**9. Neil**
Was a Surgeon Barber in Wales. Established his legal right to Pennycross in 1761. Tried and failed to recover rents. Sold the farm in 1764.

William

Donald

William

## Donald Beaton and the Memorial to Dr John

Once more, the succession had moved sideways – to another Donald, whose father was Neill, the eldest son of Doctor John (4th and last Principal Physician). Neill had not inherited the Pennycross lands himself, as his cousin Fergus outlived him, but his son Donald inherited the farm and the family manuscripts in 1674. Once he had taken over the lands, one of the first things he did was to commission a grave slab to be erected in Relig Ohrain (St Oran's graveyard) on Iona for his grandfather Doctor John, which gives another indication of the high esteem in which the doctor had been held.

The upper part of the slab bears an oval armorial medallion, carved in false-relief and features a martlet (a bird like a swallow), two sets of three cushions and three boars' heads. Above these is foliage decoration.

Dr John Beaton's graveslab in the cloisters at Iona Abbey (photo by N. Welsh). Drawing detailing the inscription on the graveslab (from H.D. Graham, *Antiquities of Iona*, 1850).

The Cathedral in Iona with the Reilig Òdhrain in the middle ground. An aquatint engraving by William Daniell from his *A Voyage Round the Coasts of Britain*, 1815-18.

The inscription around the margin of the slab reads: 'HIC IACET IOANN/ES BE-TONVS / MACLENORVM FAMILIE MEDIC(VS) / QVI MORT/V(VS) EST 19 NOWEMBR/IS / ANNO DOMINI 1657 ET ETATIS SVE 63 / DONALD-VS BETON/VS ME FECET 1674' which translates as 'Here lies John Beaton, physician to the Maclean family, who died 19 November 1657 aged 63. Donald Beaton made me 1674'

A second inscription under the medallion reads: 'ECCE CADIT IACVLO VI / CTR-ICI MORTIS INIQVE Q / VI TOTIES ALIOS SOLVER/AT IPSE MALIS. SOLE' or 'Behold, he who had so often freed others from their ills falls to the conquering dart of overpowering death. Glory be to God alone'.[68]

In 1657, as a young man of hardly more than twenty, it is thought that Donald signed one of the existing manuscripts (Laing MS) in Gaelic script as Domhnall MacBheathadh. It appears that he had received some classical training from his grandfather Doctor John, as at that time it is doubtful that physicians were still going to the continent for their classical training. The type of medical training was changing and also the Macleans had more pressing demands on their inadequate financ-es at this time of general disruption.

This disruption affected Donald in other ways too. He is mentioned in papers relating to the Macleans of Duart as being 'put to the horn' (denounced as a rebel) by the Campbells of Argyll in 1675, along with many others in Mull.[69] He is described there as 'Donald Bittoune in Pennycross'. Two other inhabitants of Pennycross are named: Hector McIloray and Donald McIlchallum; they would probably have been sub-tenants, from whom the Beatons received rent. With little or no remuneration coming in from medical treatments and consultations, the Beaton family in residence would have needed another source of income.

That same year of 1675 saw at least one member of Donald's family, his son James, being required to support his patron in the seemingly never-ending conflict between the Macleans and Campbells. In later years, James told Martin Martin, 'Being in the Isle of Mull' he was 'called by some of the MacLeans to go along with them to attack a vessel belonging to the Earl of Argyll who was coming to possess Mull by force.' This is assumed to have been a ship carrying provisions from Leith in support of the projected Campbell expedition in 1675, which was attacked in the month of September off the coast of Ardnamurchan.[70] The Beatons may not have retained their official title of An t-Ollamh Muileach – but they were still required to assist the clan when necessary.

During Donald's tenure of both Pennycross and the Beaton Library of medieval manuscripts, it must have been clear to members of the family that suitable and efficacious succession was becoming very hard to achieve. In these difficult times, their material circumstances suffered, as did everybody's, and their medical competence continued to diminish.

At Donald's death, some time before 1700, the succession was split. The lands of Pennycross went sideways again to Malcolm, Fergus's son, but the treasured manuscripts were inherited by Donald's uncle, Rev. John Beaton, described as 'the last scholar of the Beaton family in Mull'.[71]

## Rev. John Beaton, Scholar and Keeper of Manuscripts

The Rev. John Beaton was second son of the Dr John Beaton who had been the fourth, last and 'most illustrious physician'. Because his cousin Fergus had succeeded Rev. John's father, and his elder brother Neill was also a skilled and qualified physician long before their father died, his prospects in full-time medicine were bleak. So, he made the Church his chosen career and became minister of the parish of Kilninian.[72]

Although Rev. John was never destined to inherit the Beaton medical title – nor the lands of Pennycross – he did inherit the family collection of manuscripts, mostly in Gaelic, which had been amassed and passed down in the family since the first Beaton went abroad for his classical medical training. At this point, we don't know how many manuscripts made up this collection; all we can say is that there were undoubtedly many more than survive today.

Rev. John was living through a time of warfare and unrest, which, as has been noted, was mostly instigated by the Macleans of Duart

Sir John Maclean, 20th clan chief. Although chief of the clan at the time of the proposed invasion of Mull by the Campbells in 1675, he was only 4 years old, and was sent away to Cairnburgh Castle for safety. After the Battle of Killiecrankie in 1689, he, along with many other Jacobites, went into exile in France, where at the age of 23 his portrait was painted by one of the French court painters. The portrait now hangs in the Great Hall of Duart Castle, Isle of Mull, and is one of the oldest pieces of personal property in the possession of the current chief, Sir Lachlan Maclean of Duart, by whose courtesy this illustration is reproduced.

and the Campbells of Argyll. He supported the Macleans and suffered because of it; there is a note on one of the Beaton manuscripts relating to his situation. He wrote, 'I am tormented this day by cold and hunger and not of my own will.'[73] Things improved slightly in 1681 when the Campbells were ordered to surrender captured arms, ammunition and strongholds, including Duart Castle. The Rev. John was one of four men named by the Privy Council to accept the surrender. He took the opportunity to petition on his own behalf, claiming he was destitute 'through the general devastationes and hairshipes committed by the Campbells on Mull.'[74] Sadly, the privations which John had to endure didn't stop at his living conditions. It seems that some of the precious Beaton manuscripts, which had been put into his care when Donald died, fell prey to the general devastation. How many were lost, we do not know. Following the Bill of Rights of 1689,[75] the General Assembly met in 1690, and rejecting the Episcopacy (a legacy of the Stuart Kings), finally settled the

Portrait of Edward Lhuyd, naturalist, botanist, linguist, geographer, antiquary, 1709 (from T.R. Roberts, *Eminent Welshmen*, a biographical dictionary of Welshmen who have attained distinction, 1908).

reformed Scottish Church as Presbyterian. One of the results of this was that many ministers of the old Episcopalian Church felt out of place.[76] John was deprived of the living at Kilninian in 1701 and did what many another Episcopalian minister did – went to Ireland, possibly job-hunting. He took with him the Beaton library of treasured manuscripts.[77]

It was at this time (1699-1700) that Edward Lhuyd met up with this 'poor sojourning clergyman' as Beaton was described – together with his manuscripts.[78] Lhuyd was Keeper of the Ashmolean Museum in Oxford in 1681. A distinguished scholar, he was requested to undertake a survey of all the Celtic countries and in May 1697, Lhuyd left Oxford to undertake his great tour, lasting four years, through Wales, Ireland, parts of Scotland, Cornwall and Brittany. The survey was to comprise natural history, geology, history, archaeology and philology – this last because Lhuyd was aware that a knowledge of the Celtic languages was indispensable for anyone trying to achieve a comprehensive survey of the Celtic countries.[79]

So it was fortuitous indeed for these two great scholars to meet in Ireland, as they did. John Beaton's collection of Gaelic manuscripts was of enormous interest to Lhuyd, and Beaton was able to help Lhuyd pronounce the Gaelic, compile a grammar, translate the language, and answer many questions – not just about the language, but also about the history of the Celts, their customs, beliefs, archaeology, places of interest – in fact any and every subject that came to mind. There was also a suggestion that Beaton should prepare a précis of the contents of all his manuscripts, a work which would have been of immeasurable value and interest to succeeding generations. Sadly, the plan fell through, partly because there was a lack of financial support and partly because Rev. John Beaton was often from home, having to rely on help from his friends and supporters.

The last written reference we have from the hand of the Rev. John Beaton is a note written in a manuscript on 20 June 1710, preceded by the remark, 'I am oppressed by trouble of mind.'[80] He died before 1715, when his widow remarried. His death marked the end of the line for the Pennycross branch of the Beaton medical kindred; he was the last learned representative of a family that had produced scholars as well as medical practitioners for many generations.[81] However, the family itself survived and retained an interest in the Pennycross area for some years to come.

## Hanging On – The Last Gasp

### Malcolm Beaton, Who Surrendered His Sword

The succession to the lands at Pennycross shifted sideways once more – to Fergus's son, Malcolm. Why it did not go to Donald's son,

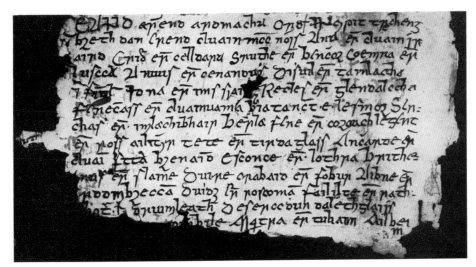

The opening passage from the *Triads of Ireland*, copied for Edward Lhuyd by Rev. John Beaton in 1700. This manuscript, later catalogued as MS.H.4.8 in Trinity College Dublin, was reproduced in *Edward Lhuyd in the Scottish Highlands* by John Lorne Campbell and Derick Thomson, 1963.

Breacachadh Castle, Coll, a tower house built in the fifteenth century. Beside it stands the newer castle, also known as Breacachadh House, constructed in the mid-eighteenth century. Published in *Coll and Tiree: Their Prehistoric Forts and Ecclesiastical Antiquities, with Notices of Ancient Remains in the Treshnish Isles* by Erskine Beveridge, 1903.

James, who was a surgeon in North Uist, is not known. It may have had something to do with the fact that Fergus's wife, Malcolm's mother, was still living at Pennycross and continued to do so until her death in 1718. Whatever the reason, it was Malcolm who was to take over the farm at Pennycross, although he was not trained in the old ways and possibly never practised medicine at all.

When referring to the Beaton family in 1702, Mr John Maclean of Kilninian said: 'They had an heritable right to so much land while they could so much as draw blood, which they yet enjoy. Mr. John Beaton being the only scholar of their race, has fallen heir to all their books and manuscripts.'[82] This would indicate that Malcolm, the current heritor, was not competent to do much else than 'draw blood' and certainly he never had the keeping of the manuscripts.

It was during Malcolm's tenure of Pennycross that the prolonged warfare on the island and further afield was brought to a temporary end, following the collapse of the Jacobite Rising of 1715. The following year, in Breacachadh Castle on the island of Coll, all the 'gentlemen of Mull', as well as the officers of the Clan Maclean battalion, surrendered their arms to James Campbell of Stonefield, Justice and Sheriff Depute of Argyll. This was another downward step for the Clan Maclean, as although they did not know it then, it was the last time the Macleans were to be united as a military unit under the command of their own officers. Among the men listed, there were only two from Pennycross:

*Peinicross*
*Malcolm Beaton of Pennicross*
*dilated by his neighbours to have been in the rebellion.*
*was not in the district – handed in one sword and one pistol*
*John McAllen VcAllen*
*was not in the rebellion. [Maclean of] Broloss took away his gun and his sword* [83]

It seems probable that John McAllen VcAllen was a tenant – and he will be mentioned again later in the Beaton story, which is not quite finished. It is highly unlikely that Malcolm took part in any of the battles during the Jacobite Rising, but it was common knowledge that the whole family were and had always been supporters of the Macleans. It is believed that Malcolm died soon after this event. He had no sons, but his mother, as has been mentioned, remained at Pennycross and died in 1718.

## Edmund Beaton, Escapee

Sometime around the time of Malcolm's death, Sir Hector Maclean (21st clan chief, 1703-1750) took a hand in the affairs of this family of former physicians. This is interesting, as the post of An t-Ollamh Muileach had effectively ceased to exist some years previously.

Although born in Calais, Sir Hector had lived with his relative Donald Maclean of Coll from the age of 4 years until he was 18. He then went to university in Edinburgh. It was during this early period in his life that he took an interest in the Beaton family and their lands at Pennycross.[84] It is not known why Edmund was the family member chosen to be the successor to the lands of Pennycross, although it may have had something to do with the fact that he was son of the Rev. John and grandson of the renowned Doctor John.

Perhaps because of his own interest in education, Sir Hector Maclean decided to help Edmund Beaton, although in 1719 he also repossessed the Beaton family lands of Pennycross. This was probably to ensure that the land was properly managed, as he had been planning to pay for Edmund's education from the rent of the farm. Edmund, being 'then very young, Sir Hector MacLean caused take care of him and applied the rents of Peinnacross for three years towards breeding him a surgeon'.[85] However, this plan was not destined to be successful, as Edmund *'ran off from his apprenticeship to England'.*[86] This is the last indication we have of Sir Lachlan's interest in him! However, as will be seen, he did maintain an interest in the land. Some years later, Edmund's younger brother Neill wrote that he had died in Jamaica in the year 1758 or 1759.[87]

# 3

# *Uncovering What Happened to the Former Beaton Lands of Pennycross*

## Years of Neglect; Farming Practice and Unsympathetic Landlords

It appears that the Beatons did not remain at Pennycross for very long after the exile of the Duart Macleans. Once young Edmund Beaton had indicated his unwillingness to follow in the footsteps of his illustrious forebears, by running away from his schooling, there was no successor to the farm of Pennycross and 'the Lands stood for some time wasted without any person claiming right to them'.[88]

Sir Hector Maclean, as a direct descendant of the chief who had first given the land to Andrew Beaton, was advised that as the Beatons had produced no more heirs to the property, the lands reverted to the Macleans. He repossessed the farm from 1719 onwards, until in 1732 he sold the land to a Lachlan Maclean, a merchant in Glasgow, for £100 sterling, which was thought to be the going rate. It is unlikely that Lachlan ever lived on the farm, merely sub-letting it and being in receipt of rents. Sir Hector Maclean's specific reason for granting Pennycross to other owners than Beatons was

that none of them had been 'entered with me or my predecessours [as physicians] for these fourty years and upwards'.[97]

The fact that there were no successors to the lands and title did not mean that it was empty of inhabitants. When Malcolm Beaton handed over his weapons in 1716, it may be remembered that another man was listed – John McAllen VcAllen. There would doubtless have been others – the farm had to be worked. Pennycross would not have been communally tenanted, as were the surrounding farms at that time, but the succession of Beaton families who had been granted the lease would have needed outdoor servants to undertake all the work required.

Farming practice was basic and very hard work for relatively little result. Arable land was divided into strips – 'rigs' – and planted with oats and bere, an early variety of barley. Once the grain was harvested, it was dried in kilns, which were usually built a little way from the houses because of the danger of fire. It was milled with hand querns, or, on larger

The cas chrom, literally, 'crooked foot', a foot plough used to dig the 'rigs' or lazy beds
which would then be manured with seaweed, brought up from the shore in creels.
(Sketch by Jackie Le May, courtesy of Mark Le May.)

farms, small horizontal mills. (Potatoes were not introduced until after the Beatons left the land, about 1740.) Seaweed was used as manure, the men doing the heavy work of cutting and floating the weed in February before they went off fishing. Women mostly carried the seaweed from the shore in creels.

The physical conditions of Mull have always made it more suitable for the raising of livestock than for the cultivation of crops, and islanders have mainly depended on their livestock ever since their remote ancestors first became herdsmen rather than hunters. The Highland cattle breed known as Black Cattle, is one of the oldest in the world. Dairy products, butter and cheese, were the main source of food for a considerable part of the year, and the beasts were almost the only way in which farmers or tenants could earn money to pay their rents, though much of the rent was paid in kind. Andrew Beaton's lease in 1572 contains reference to '3 st[ones] oatmeal, 2 st[ones] cheese & 1 Boll of Malt'[54] which had to be paid. Butter, cream and eggs could also be part of the agreement. Small, short-tailed sheep were also kept, mostly for the use of the residents, not for sale. They were often housed at night, tethered by day and kept in relatively small numbers for their milk and wool. It was not until the Beatons were leaving Pennycross that the coarse-woolled sheep of the Borders, which could be kept all year round on the higher hills, were beginning to be introduced.

It was yet another Maclean, John of Killean, factor to Maclean of Duart, who had the lease of the Farm from Lachlan Maclean, Glasgow. He approached Malcolm Beaton's sister, Ann, who with her husband had the tenancy of the farm of Dererach, on the other side of Loch Scridain, and tried to obtain from her the legal papers concerning the farm which had last been in the possession of her deceased brother. When she would not relinquish them, John Mclean threatened to turn her out of Dererach. However, she stood up to him and would not surrender the papers.

John Mclean was not a sympathetic tenant of Pennycross. In later years, he was accused of stripping the house of its contents and doing a good deal of damage. It seems unlikely that he was of a mind to maintain the Beaton Physic Garden. There is no documentary evidence which has yet come to light as to what happened to the Garden during these bleak

Lands associated with the ancient farm of Pennycross, looking north across Loch Scridain to Ben More. The house at Dererach, associated with Ann, Malcolm Beaton's sister, can be seen on the north side of the loch below the afforested area (photo by Nigel Burch).

years. However, it is interesting to note that there were at least two physicians, though not Beatons, living fairly close by at the time. The nearest was Dr Alexander Maclean (1725 to 1786) from Killunaig (of whom more later). There was also Dr Hector Maclean from Gruline (1704 to 1786). Both these men would have known of the famous garden and may possibly have tried in some way to preserve the plants there, especially those more uncommon in the area.

## A Bill for Lawburrows, Neighbours from Hell[89]

During the bleak years when the farm had been sold to Lachlan Maclean of Glasgow, and then let to John Mclean of Killean, there were still Beatons living on the Pennycross lands. We know this because of a strange case of Lawburrows. This is a little-known civil action in Scots law initiated by one person who is afraid of possible violence from another. Interestingly, this Act of 1429 is still in force today. The bill was taken out in 1742 by Alexander McGilvra of Pennyghael, the neighbouring estate proprietor against Margaret Beaton and her children, who were named as:

Charles MC Ean vic Allan (Charles Allan)
Ewn MC Ean vic Allan (Hugh Allan)
Allan MC Ean vic Allan (Allan Allan)
Katherine Nin Ean vic Allan (Catherine Allan)

It seems likely that Margaret was Malcolm Beaton's daughter and had married the John McAllen VcAllen who was named as living at Pennycross in 1716, when the men of Mull were required to hand in their weapons. The action that Alexander McGilvra took was to prevent Margaret and her children from threatening him. Exactly what they were doing is not known, but they were obviously not the best of neighbours to have.

The Bill declares that the family 'having Conceived a deadly hatred Evil will & Malice Causeless Against the Complainer Upon what occasion he knows not . . . daily and Continually trouble & oppress the said Complainer & tennants Servants Cottars & Dependers in the peaceable possession of their lands ffarms Grass pasturage Rooms possessions Goods & Gear and threaten & Menace the said Complainer & his foresaids for their bodily harm & slaughter to bereave them of their Lives and lyin wait for that effect and to burn their houses & hough[90] their Cattle & oyrways Molest trouble & oppress the said Complainer . . .'

What came of this action is not known.

## Land in Limbo

As has been seen, Edmund never returned to Pennycross to take up his inheritance. But all the time he was alive, he was the 'legitimate' heir to the lands according to the old dispensation, and no-one else in the family could do anything about it. Because the tenant, John

Mclean of Killean, had stripped the Beaton house, the remaining Beaton family members would presumably have been living somewhere else.[91]

Also, fairly soon after Sir Hector had claimed back the farm, it was pointed out that Pennycross was actually the property of the Duke of Argyll, and that he therefore had no right to sell or lease out the land or have anything to do with the rents. However 'it was not until 1756 that Argyll acted, taking the lands of Pennycross into his own hands "as being properly superior" thereof and dispossessing Lachlan MacLean.'[92]

It was a mess and once again, the lands were in limbo.

## Neill Beaton Reclaims the Land

Neill Beaton was the youngest son of the Rev. John Beaton, who had been described as the last scholarly Beaton on Mull. It will be remembered that Neill's elder brother Edmund was supposed to inherit the lands of Pennycross, but had run away from his school, never to return. All the time Edmund was alive, no-one else from the family could do anything about the situation. Then, in 1760, Neill Beaton came forward, claiming that as his brother had died in 1755, he (Neill) was now the rightful heir to the lands.[93] He had been living in Wales for some years, and had only just heard of his brother's death.

He wrote two memorials as to why he was authorised to inherit, which include a partial genealogy of his immediate family. He also stated that he was 'skilled in Bottany and other parts of surgery being bred a Surgeon Barber in Wales'.[94] A Mr Archibald Campbell, Writer to the Signet, wrote a report on his first memorial. He concluded that although the exclusive privileges of Surgeon and Medical Practitioner to the Macleans of Duart no longer existed, Neill's claim was just, in that he was a true descendant, and heir to his great-grandfather Malcolm, and the lands of Pennycross should be restored to him. Neill won his appeal and was duly put in possession of Pennycross in 1761. However, he was not completely satisfied, as he felt that the family had been cheated of their income from the farm over the last 30-odd years. In 1762 he began legal proceedings to recover the rents of Pennycross from 1726 to 1756 (some £200 Sterling)[95] from Lachlan Maclean, the Glasgow merchant, and John Mclean of Killean, one-time factor to Duart. He also sued for damages of £50 from Mclean, 'as the value of the damage done to the said Mansion House of Peincross . . . his illegaly and unwarrantably carrying off . . . the timber partitions & Joists'. Unsurprisingly, both Lachlan and John Mclean refused to comply.[96]

Whether Neill ever intended to move back to the old family home of Pennycross is doubtful, as in 1764 he sold the land. Perhaps he just wanted restitution for the years of lost rent, as even after the sale, he continued the legal battle for the money.[97] So the farm of Pennycross left the Beaton family for the last time, although it wasn't the last time that it was associated with medicine, as it was purchased in 1765 by the local doctor, Alexander Maclean, surgeon in Brolas. We know this because in April of that year he was congratulated by his first cousin, Hector Maclean of Gruline, also a physician, for his acquisition.[98] Perhaps he bought it because of its celebrated Physic Garden and association with illustrious physicians of former centuries. Alexander was the son of Charles Maclean, tacksman of Killunaig and Torranbeg, and in 1760 had married Una, a daughter of Alexander McGilvra of Pennyghael – who had instigated the action of Lawburrows against Margaret Beaton back in 1742. Following his purchase of the farm, Alexander became Maclean of Pennycross. The land stayed in the hands of this family until 1819, when it was sold to William MacGillivray as part of the Pennyghael Estate, for which sale the Langlands estate map was prepared.

# 4

# *Kith and Kin*
# *The Beatons of Dervaig*

The Beatons of Pennycross were not the only doctors to be employed by the Macleans of Duart and to be practising on Mull. This was not uncommon – other clan chiefs employed several physicians. The Isle of Mull is extensive, and Pennycross being in the south, it made sense to have another physician available towards the north.

The branch of the Beaton family centred at Dervaig[99] appears to have been well established there by the 1500s, and was closely related to Beatons in both Kilelane (Killallan, Renfrewshire) and Colonsay. This was an important branch of the Beaton kindred, as in fact, the earliest Beaton on record to be entitled An t-Ollamh Muileach is a James Beaton of Dervaig. He is said to have attended Alexander Fraser of Lovat on his deathbed in 1558.[100] This means that he was practising for more than 20 years before Andrew, the first Ollamh in Pennycross, had been granted his lands by Hector MacLean in 1582.

Later, around 1613-15, another member of this family was probably attending the Stewarts of Appin. This Beaton, another James, signed his name to one of the Gaelic manuscripts as 'Semus mac an ollaimh' meaning James, son of the Principal Physician,[101] and it is quite possible that this second James may also have been An t-Ollamh Muileach for a time. This occurred around the time of the death of Donald, third of the Pennycross Physicians, which appears to have been not long after that of his father Malcolm and it is surmised that for various reasons there was no other member of the Pennycross family immediately 'suitable' to take on the role and that perhaps James of Dervaig assumed the mantle for a short period.

It is highly likely that the Beatons of Dervaig and the Beatons of Pennycross were in regular contact.

What is definitely known is that this second James Beaton contributed to several of the Gaelic manuscripts which eventually ended up in the Pennycross collection. In addition to this he assisted the main scribe in copying out Bernard Gordon's *Lilium Medicinae*, a treatise which was already famous. His distinctive Gaelic script can be found at the point in the transcription where it is stated that the manuscript was being written in October 1621 at Duart in Mull.[102] These manuscripts ended up in the Pennycross 'library' – two sections from one of them having already been bound together by Malcolm (the second Ollamh from Pennycross).

It is also known from his signature that Neill, eldest son of John, the last Ollamh of Pennycross, assisted James of Dervaig in writing a version of the *Lilium Medicinae*[103] when he was quite a young man and was

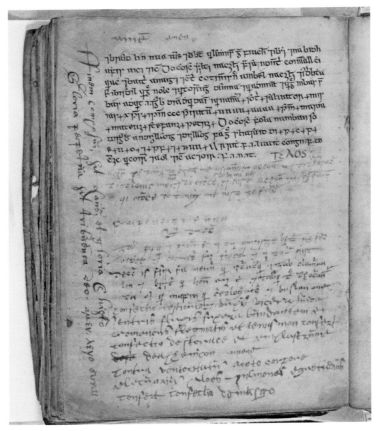

One page of the manuscript in James' hand, written while he was staying with the Stewarts in Appin. It contains treatments and charms for various conditions, including how to ensure the birth of a male child (National Library of Scotland Adv. MS 72.1.3, f.80v). This page also shows how the original script was added to over the years by succeeding physicians. These additions varied from notes on treatments, fresh discoveries or even personal comments.

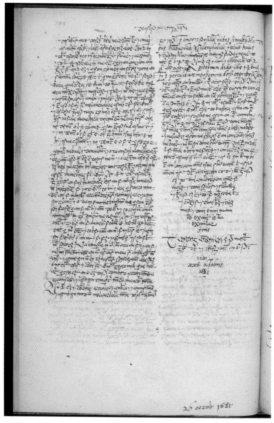

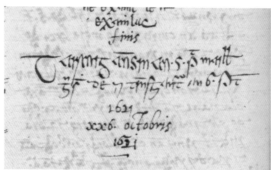

This page of the manuscript was written by James and is the completion of one section of the text; at the end of the section (right) is the date October 1621. More details of this manuscript can be found in the next chapter (National Library of Scotland Advocates MS 18.2.11, f.102v).

possibly his pupil sometime before 1650. Yet another James Beaton was still practising medicine in Mull in 1771. The registrar of the parish of Kilninian and Kilmore made a note to the effect that this James was paid in part *for curing Jean McLauchlane'* and was paid in full twelve days later.[104]

So, it seems that this second Beaton family on Mull was in possession of the office of An t-Ollamh Muileach both before their kin at Pennycross and also for a time in the first half of the seventeenth century. This would be quite in keeping with the kin-based rules of succession. However, this did not mean that the Dervaig family had a right to the lands at Pennycross. What it does mean is that this branch of the family was practising on Mull for much longer than their more well-known Pennycross relatives.

There is a possibility that one of the Jameses was the subject of one of the legends connected with the Beaton Doctors,[105] although the specific Beaton and the specific king are not mentioned (see below).

# 5

# *The Beaton Legacy*

## Legends concerning the Beatons

There are at least eight well-known legends connected with the Beaton family of physicians. Exactly how many of these are definitely connected with the Pennycross or Dervaig branches of the family is not known. As with all legends, they are traditional and ancient stories, popularly regarded as historical, but not authenticated. Sometimes the legend appears to have a purpose: perhaps to explain natural phenomena that earlier generations did not understand; perhaps to convey a moral message of some sort; or perhaps it served to exaggerate a relatively true, historical account. As these stories were handed down orally, they were bound to change in the telling, so there can never be a definitive version. What the hidden purposes behind these legends were, is now a matter of conjecture . . .

## How An t-Ollamh Muileach Got His Lands – Two Tales for the Same Event

This first legend comes from a collection of tales of the Scottish Highlands gathered originally in the Gaelic language during the mid-nineteenth century by John Dewar, a woodman in the employ of the 8th Duke of Argyll. He travelled round the West Highlands visiting old people and listening to their tales. He later copied them out in longhand and delivered them to Inveraray Castle, where they were bound into the volumes which are now known as 'The Dewar Manuscripts'.

It happened that Maclean of Aros held a secret grudge against MacGillivray of Glencannel, and when the two were dining together, Maclean drew his sword and took off the upper part of MacGillivray's skull.

MacGillivray survived this dreadful attack and was taken home by his attendants, who called for the Ollamh Muileach to attend him. It was no easy matter, for the exposed brain was covered only by a thin membrane, but the Mull doctor was skilled, the wound began to heal and MacGillivray made good progress.

One day Maclean of Aros met the doctor on his way to see his patient and enquired of his progress. When told that MacGillivray

How An t'Ollamh Muileach got his lands (illustration by Miek Zwamborn).

was progressing well and would soon be able to get up from his bed, Maclean demanded that the Ollamh Muileach should kill him. The Ollamh refused, saying, 'I will not kill him, he never did me any harm – My business is to heal men, not kill them.' However Maclean offered to give him lands at Pennycross as a reward for doing so. Finally the doctor agreed – but insisted on being given the written right to the lands before the deed was done.

Before the doctor reached MacGillivray's house he picked a stalk of rye grass and carried it with him. Arriving, he found the patient feeling better, but insisted on removing the bandages and inspecting the wound. He looked at it for a short time, then began rubbing the membrane covering the brain with the head of the grass stalk until he had made a hole through it. MacGillivray realised what he was doing and drew his sword to strike the doctor, but the latter succeeded in dodging the blow. However, this effort was too much for MacGillivray, who died from his efforts.

So Maclean of Aros took possession of MacGillivray's lands of Glencannel and the Ollamh Muileach got possession of the lands of Pennycross.

## An Alternative Tale as to How the Beatons Came to Possess Pennycross

A re-telling of this legend at any length has not yet been discovered, but the essence of the story was told to Thomas Scott Muir in 1861 by Miss Maclean of Pennycross and quoted in his book *Characteristics of Old Church Architecture etc in the Mainland and Western Islands of Scotland*.

From time immemorial, the Beatons were physicians, tradition says originally from Ireland. So eminent were they, that the Kings of Scotland had them at their Courts, particularly James 2nd . . . They were all along physicians to the Macleans of Duart. I never heard of any professional neighbours they had in this island *(Miss Maclean didn't appear to accept the medical branch of the Beaton family who lived at Dervaig.)* Tradition says that they had brothers in Skye and Islay, thought highly of as medical men. Maclean of Duart was wounded by a poisoned arrow, and his case thought hopeless: Beaton, to the wonder of the world, established a cure, for which the laird presented him with Pennycross in perpetuity.

As there is no 'story' as such attached to this tradition of the Beatons' arrival in Pennycross, one wonders if it was made up specifically to suggest a more acceptable version of the Beaton accession to the farm. In the mid-nineteenth century it was good taste to hide the legs of tables, so perhaps the violent and somewhat scurrilous version of the tale was unacceptable to the ladies of the time, who, after all, were very proud of the illustrious family who had lived on their estate. And who can believe in an already celebrated physician who would deliberately kill to obtain land? It is all conjecture.

## Origins of the Healing Power of the Beatons

One legend tells of how Doctor John Beaton acquired his powers as a physician. As a youngster he visited Ireland to learn from a doctor there. He took with him a stick cut from a rowan tree near his home. When his instructor saw this, he told John to go back home and seek out a white snake which lived at the foot of the tree. John did this and returned to Ireland with the captured snake. The Irish doctor dropped it into a pot of boiling water and then went out, asking John to watch the pot but on no account to drink any of the liquid from it.

John settled to his task, but after a while a few drops of the scalding liquid bubbled out on to his arm. Without thinking he licked it to relieve the pain. On his return the physician questioned John and heard what had happened. He then revealed to the lad that the liquid gave great powers of healing to the first person who drank it. Thus John was enabled to become the 'illustrious physician' from Pennycross.

It is interesting to note that the symbol for medicine and healing, which has been in existence since the time of the ancient Greeks, is the Rod of Asclepius. This symbol incorporates

Origins of the healing power of the Beatons (illustration by Miek Zwamborn).

a serpent entwined around a rod or staff – the two most important items figuring in the legend; surely no coincidence.

## Laughter Is the Best Medicine

There are several versions of this tale, in which the patient is either Maclean of Aros, Duart or Lochbuy; the Ollamh Muileach in question is either Doctor John or Seamus – James of Dervaig. But this really doesn't matter; the heart of the story remains the same.

At one time Maclean of Lochbuy was dangerously ill from a huge abscess near the larynx, which interfered with his breathing but was impossible to reach with instruments. The best medical practitioners of the day had come from the mainland and were in constant attendance, but could do nothing for the patient.

Finally, An t-Ollamh Muileach, Doctor John Beaton from Pennycross, was sent for. He asked to see Maclean alone, and having examined him, very quickly diagnosed the problem, realising that the only cure would be some sudden, violent exertion of the lungs which would burst the abscess. But how to bring this about in such a weakened patient?

In front of the amazed, and probably horrified Maclean, An t-Ollamh Muileach grabbed the shovel by the hearth, took down his breeches and proceeded to fill it with his own faeces (poo!) which he then roasted over

Laughter is the best medicine (illustration by Miek Zwamborn).

the fire until it was dry enough to be powdered. The unlikely preparation was then wrapped in paper and placed half-open on the bedside table. All this was done in silence. Maclean was speechless and Doctor John still said nothing, merely putting a cautionary finger to his lips and going to sit near the fire. The banished medical men were then allowed to return to the room. Beaton sat on, seeming to pay no attention to the attempts his professional brethren were making to analyse the chemical properties of this unknown new medicine.

The sick man was an attentive witness of all that the perplexed physicians were doing; they threw questions at him, but he merely waved weakly at the parcel of brown powder and murmured that Beaton had given no advice. They poked and smelled the powder but could make nothing of it. However, when he saw them one by one taking some of the powder and tasting it, he could contain his mirth no longer. The convulsions of suppressed laughter burst the abscess in his throat and, in a few minutes, procured the relief he so much needed.

## A Royal Joke

A member of the Beaton family was called to the bedside of an ailing king, as he and his advisors had lost confidence in the court physicians. These royal doctors were annoyed and insulted by this; they decided to obstruct the 'intruder' in his diagnosis. They substituted the King's urine with that from a cow. However, when Beaton examined the sample, he soon realised the trick that had been played. His comment to the court physicians was along the lines of, 'If you gentlemen will open up his Majesty, you will find him in calf.' The King was given a new treatment, and, of course, was soon restored to health. This tale was made into a poem and then a song, which can be found in several old publications.[106]

## The Beaton Treatments for Rheumatism and for Sore Eyes

These two legends are recorded by J.P. Maclean (*History of the Isle of Mull*, 1923, Chap. XI, Medicine and Its Offices).

It is related that the wife of a man who was suffering from rheumatism came to Pennycross to consult An t-Ollamh Muileach. When the doctor visited the patient, he took with him a birch rod. He got the man up from his bed and instructed his wife to apply the rod violently to his back and chase him around until told to stop. The doctor forced her to continue this treatment of her husband until the poor man was perspiring freely, by which time he had become more supple and freed from pain.

The second of these legends concerns a man who went to see Ollamh Muileach to be treated for sore eyes. After an examination, Doctor Beaton pronounced that he was more in danger of another problem – that very soon, horns would appear on his knees. As can be imagined, the man was greatly alarmed at this diagnosis and appealed to the doctor to save him from this disaster.

The Beaton treatment for rheumatism … and for sore eyes (illustration by Miek Zwamborn).

'There is only one way,' said the doctor. 'You must keep your hands on your knees for three weeks. At the end of that period, come to me, so that I can see how you are getting on.'

At the specified time, the man visited the Doctor at Pennycross.

'Well,' said the doctor, 'Have the horns made their appearance?'

'No,' replied the patient.

'And have you followed my advice?'

'Oh, yes,' replied the man, 'I have kept my hands on my knees day and night, just as you said.'

'Good – and how are your eyes?' enquired the Doctor.

'My eyes? Oh, they are quite well,' replied the patient.

'Very well; go home, make your mind easy about the horns – and don't rub your eyes!'

## The Birth of Murchadh Gearr (Murdo the Short)

This tale was recorded from Donald Morrison who was born in Ardtun in the Ross of Mull in 1885. It was transcribed and translated by Alan Bruford.[107] As Donald told it:

'Some say, according to tradition that it happened like this . . .' the then Maclean of Lochbuy had been captured by Maclean of Duart, and imprisoned 'in an island out there at the back of Staffa, which they call Cairnburg'. Although Lochbuy was getting on in years, Maclean, not wanting anything untoward to happen, 'left the ugliest woman in Mull with him, to prepare his food, and I suppose they had all the facilities they had in those days. That was going on fine, but events took another turn: the woman who was in Cairnburg with

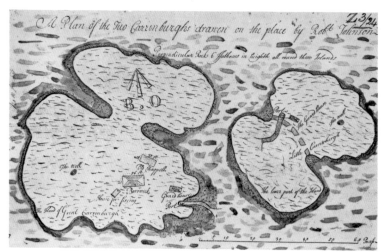

Board of Ordnance drawing of the two islands of Cairnburg, Cairn na Burgh More and Cairn na Burgh Beg, 1741.

The frog and the nettle (illustration by Miek Zwamborn).

him grew – she wasn't very well' (in fact it was discovered that she was pregnant) 'and she was sent, taken away from there and taken to Torloisk'. This was also Duart territory.

An t-Ollamh Muileach from Pennycross was sent for, as he was physician to Maclean of Duart.

'And this man, he was asked to come and see to the woman when it was needed, and he said he would. And Duart said to him, "If it's a son, strangle him, but if it's a daughter, let her live."'

When the child was born, it was indeed a son, but when Ollamh Muileach returned to Duart, he told Maclean that it was a daughter.

'And he was kept in hiding until he grew up; he was up in a place up here they call Glencannel, with some of the MacGillivrays

in hiding there, until he grew up to be a man, and then he came to the fore. And yes, you know . . . if there hadn't been anyone to succeed the man who was in prison in Cairnburg – you see, Duart would have had Lochbuy land along with the rest! . . . That's the story I heard handed down.'[108]

## The Frog and the Nettle

The tale is told that Doctor John's only daughter became chronically ill of some disease that baffled diagnosis and treatment. In spite of their care, the young woman sank from day to day and, ultimately, she died. Upon dissection, her father discovered a live frog embedded in her intestines.

It is said that he kept this poor creature for a long time, giving it food of whatever

# The Beaton Surname as Used in the Manuscripts

Spellings varied considerably over the years. At one stage these men wrote their surname in Gaelic as **MacBeathadh**, occasionally **MacBheath**. In an early dated signature to the Islay Charter of 1408, the form, so far as it can be read, is **Fercos MacBetha**. In the Laing Manuscript, under the date 1587, is an entry from **Giolla Colaim Mic Giolla Enndris MicDomhnaill MicBhethath**; and later dated 1657, the form is **Domhnall McBethadh**.

In the seventeenth century the form Beaton came into use among the family. In 1638 **Dr James Beatoun[e]** visited Islay. In 1674 **Donaldus Betonus** erected a tombstone in Iona. In 1677 **Joannes Bettounus** wrote his name in Greek characters.

description the household had. One day he was to be away from home for some hours, leaving the servants with strict orders not to neglect the frog. They had nettle soup for dinner that day, and the frog had its share, with the alarming result that after a short while it was found dead. Everybody was fearful of the doctor's anger on hearing the news. When he came home however and was told what had happened, he cried out: 'Alas! Alas! how easily I could have cured my daughter, had I known that a medicine so simple could have counteracted a disease so treacherous.'

In regularly changing the frog's food the motive was to ascertain what would kill it. Ever after that the doctor recommended nettle soup each spring. Even to this day the older folk follow the physician's advice, nettle soup being a favourite during the season, and it is claimed to tone the system. In the present day, nettles are still recognised as containing a wide variety of nutrients and nettle soup is widely consumed.

## The Beaton Library

There are twenty-five surviving manuscripts which were either written by, or once owned by the Beatons. These are currently preserved in archives in Scotland and England. The descriptions in this chapter cover some of the most significant and best-recognised manuscripts. Apart from the Laing Manuscript, which is in the University of Edinburgh, those described here are held by the National Library of Scotland, in what was formerly the Advocates' Library.[109]

The Beaton medical kindred used many of their manuscripts as notebooks, '*Vade Mecum*', in which they stored the sum of their reading, compiled and translated from many ancient authors, including scholars such as Avicenna, Averroes, Joannes de Vigo, Bernardus Gordonus and Hippocrates.[110] They added their own comments and observations in the margins, building upon their collective knowledge, as the manuscripts were handed down from one generation to the next. The manuscript compilation was not intended for publication, but was a practical *aide memoire*. Most of the material was written in the Scottish and Irish Gaelic of the time, although some sections are written in Latin and English.

This page shows some of the notes added at various times to the main text. Many of these were made by Doctor John Beaton, the 4th Ollamh (National Library of Scotland, Adv. MS 18.2.11. f.67r).

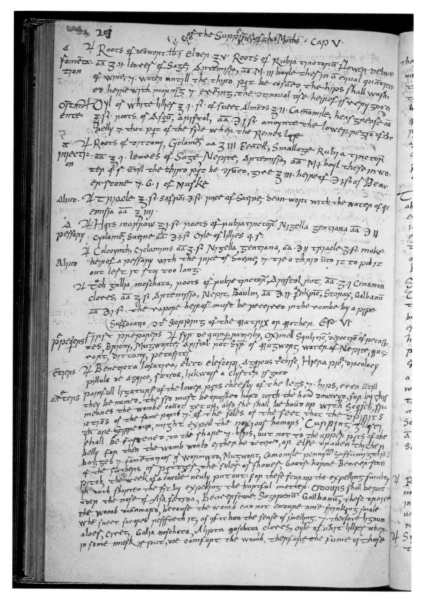

One of the pages in English ascribed to Rev. John Beaton, in which the names of various herbs can be recognised. They include sage, camomile, dittany, cyclamen, fennel, nigella, gentian, balm, bryony, mugwort, betony, wormwood and pennyroyal (National Library of Scotland, Adv. MS 18.2.11. f.185v).

## *Lilium Medicinae* from Montpellier

The *Lilium Medicinae* was written by Bernardus Gordonus, Professor of Physic at the University of Montpellier in France, and published in 1305. It is in Montpellier that one of the Beaton physicians is said to have translated the *Lilium* into Gaelic during the 1500s.[111] The work was held in high regard throughout Europe for several centuries, with its combination of medicine and philosophy influenced by Arabic scholars such as Avicenna and Averroes. It was one of the most popular original medieval works of its kind and was in all the leading European medical universities.

A number of Gaelic versions existed in Ireland and Scotland, one of which (NLS, Adv. MS 18.2.11) was in the possession of the Pennycross Beatons. It is believed to have been transcribed in October 1621 at Duart Castle, principally by James Beaton of Dervaig, Mull, with additions by Doctor John Beaton of Pennycross and Angus Beaton of Skye (see chapter on The Beaton Physicians of Pennycross).

The cost of copying a Gaelic version was high, said to be worth the same as sixty milk cows. It was also recounted that if a Beaton doctor was visiting a patient by sea, he would send the manuscript overland with a servant whenever possible, for greater security.[112]

The manuscript also contains the only surviving piece of sustained medical writing in Rev. John Beaton's hand. Although, as has been noted, he was never Ollamh Muileach, he was a distinguished scholar who had a vast medical knowledge and contributed extensively to the Beaton Library.

## The Beaton Manuscript and the Industrious Malcolm Beaton

The Beaton Manuscript (NLS, Adv. MS 72.1.2.) is a very large and incredibly varied medical compendium of some 148 pages, assembled from material originating from the Mull Beatons, with additions from Irish physicians; over 80 different hands have been identified. It is now in 13 or more sections of manuscript bound together. It has been suggested that the work of bringing the pieces together was done by 'the industrious Malcolm Beaton', and the last of the Beatons to have added to the work was his grandson the Rev. John, who died in 1715.

Who owned the manuscript next is not known, but around 1731-34, the Rev. John's manuscripts were on the market and it may well have changed hands around this time. What we do know is that it was presented to the Library of the Faculty of Advocates by the Rev. Donald MacQueen, late minister of Kilmuir in Skye sometime before 1785, the year of his death.

The pages, written on both vellum and paper, were bound in calf at the beginning of the nineteenth century. Some of the pages of former sections are missing and a few are bound in the wrong order, but considering its age, the condition of this manuscript is good

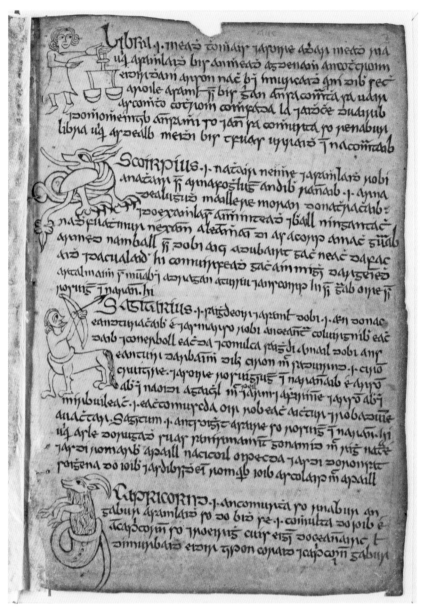

This page, written on vellum, is from the first section of the Beaton Manuscript and shows four of the twelve signs of the Zodiac and notes about the constellations (National Library of Scotland, Adv. MS 72.1.2, f.3r).

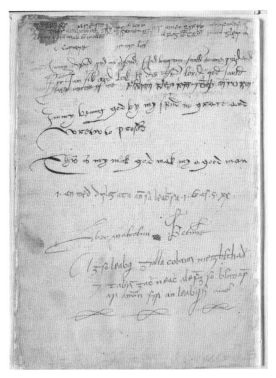

This page from the sixth section contains pen trials in various hands, including that of Neil Beaton, which reads: 'In my defend God me defend And bring my sauld to ane guid end, for I am sik and leik to die, the Lord God sauld heve mercie of me.' An unidentified hand wrote: 'This is my [mook?] god mak my a good man.' Further down the page, 'Liber Makolmi Betune' is written in the hand of Malcolm Beaton (National Library of Scotland, Adv. MS 72.1.2, f.65v).

and very little of the text is missing. It seems that Malcolm Beaton tidied up pages by trimming uneven edges and corners, which cut off some of the marginal notes. The contents are described as 'practical by medieval standards', rather than theoretical, and include material on astrology and astronomy, the calendar, botany and the Brehon law among other subjects. Later hands also added charms and prayers. What follows is a selection of just a few of the topics covered in this compendium and indicates a little of its variety and range.

The first section deals with the constellations and the signs of the Zodiac. The second, written in at least six different hands, talks of the four humours; the derivation of the names of the planets; the definitions of health and sickness; a prayer which could be used as a charm; treacle; raw and cooked diets; and includes notes on causes of disease, citing

The volvelle, or wheel chart, on this page from the eighth section was used for calculating the date of Easter. When the circular piece of vellum with a crudely drawn figure in the centre of the page is turned so that the foot indicates the most recent golden number, the outstretched hand points to the date of the coming Easter (National Library of Scotland, Adv. MS 72.1.2.f. 130v).

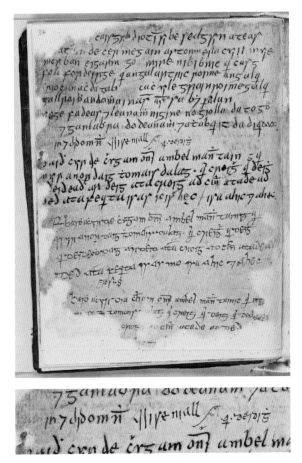

Compared to other manuscripts in the Beaton Library, this one is quite dilapidated. Pages in this section include charms and folk cures among the medical texts. At line 9 in the page above, Neil Beaton (eldest son of Doctor John) has signed his name (National Library of Scotland, Adv. MS 72.1.33, p. 34).

Jacobus de Forlivio, Avicenna, Pythagoras and Galen.

The third section, on vellum, is a tiny manuscript containing verses in Latin useful for memorising aspects of the calendar. The fourth is a really mixed bag, some notes being in English. There is a good deal of writing about urine; various charms, including a fertility charm for both women and trees; love charms; charms against felons, and another against baldness. Then there are receipts (recipes) for treacle, for poison and dying the hair golden, plus a cure for insanity.

The fifth section is also written on vellum

and contains a compilation of receipts for particular conditions, thought to be attributed to Trotula Plataerius, an eleventh-century Italian woman who was said to be one of the most knowledgeable of all women physicians. There are cures for jaundice, dropsy, scrofula, quinsy, worms, mouth ailments and bad breath. The sixth section is also on vellum and is another varied collection, beginning with Bernard of Gordon's teaching on wounds from his *Lilium Medicinae*. There are treatments for many conditions, including toothache, liver ailments and dropsy; with notes on syrups, bathing the sick, gout, apothecaries' weights and drinks made from honey.

The seventh section, again on vellum, contains cures for eye ailments and toothache; for sciatica, nose bleeding and epilepsy. There are charms against dreams and notes on rosemary, heart disease and the veins in the hand. The eighth features material on types of epilepsy; purgatives; causes of drunkenness; charms against fever, wolves, sleep, toothache, loss of blood and drowning; cures for failing eyesight; ways of ensuring safe delivery, steadying loose teeth, healing burns; and further cures for wounds, stings and bites.

The ninth section is a short one, dealing with veins and bloodletting, while the tenth is composed of small scraps of parchment, possibly cut from another book. It contains a commentary on aspects of the Brehon law on maintenance of the sick; also charms against blindness, the evil eye, burning, drowning, wounding and loss of blood; Arabic numbers

up to 100, and a cure for unwanted hair. There are also medical and physical riddles – sadly without answers; and a description of the witch Erictho.[113]

The eleventh section on vellum includes details of terminal symptoms; leprosy and its twelve varieties; wine; the effect of heat and cold on wounds; notes on drink and the tastes. It quotes Arnaldus' teachings on beans and barley; treatments for flux of the belly, dysentery, diarrhoea etc, citing Galen, Bernard and Avicenna; together with cures for scurf and scabies.

The twelfth was once the property of John Beaton and is mainly scholastic in nature. Various sections deal with more abstract concepts, such as how certain parts of the body got their names, a discussion of smells and why yew and holly retain their foliage throughout the year. Finally, the thirteenth and last section contains a complete tract on cures and specifics, presented according to their application from the head downwards. The last page details how to 'cure the stone', i.e. remove kidney or bladder stones.

## *Materia Medica*, a Medieval Pharmacology

A *Materia Medica* is a treatise about the therapeutic properties of medicines. The volume (NLS, Adv. MS 72.1.3.) is the most lavishly decorated of the surviving Gaelic manuscripts in the Beaton collection, having ornamental initials using the colours red, crimson, brown, blue and yellow. From the text it appears that

A page from the *Materia Medica* showing how the illustrator embellished the text with ornamental initials (National Library of Scotland, Adv. MS 72.1.3, f.19r).

this manuscript was in the hands of James Beaton of Dervaig, while he was attending the household of Stewart of Appin, sometime between 1613 and 1620, when he prescribed an infusion of betony for one of the women, possibly Stewart's wife. (See Chapter on the Beatons of Dervaig.) By 1677 the manuscript had passed to the Rev. John Beaton, whose contributions were in Gaelic, English, Latin and Greek. Following his death it was eventually sold to the Advocates' Library by a bookseller, Robert Freebairn, in 1736.

Neill MacBeath's Psalter, his *Vade Mecum*

This chunky little book (NLS, Adv. MS 72.1.4) is bound by stout thongs and thread to a skin cover which extends into 'tails', which would have enabled it to be tied to the physician's belt. This would have allowed it to be used as a *vade mecum* and carried around whenever the physician was working away from home.

The outside front cover has a jetton fixed to it, which has been secured like a button by means of a thong. A jetton was a reckoning counter, used on a counting board, similar to the arrangement of an abacus, but with squares in which the metal counters were placed. Jettons were an important part of government and commercial life in the Middle Ages. This particular one comes from Nuremberg,

The cover of Neill MacBeath's Psalter, showing the tails used to tie it to the physician's belt. (National Library of Scotland, Adv. MS 72.1.4).

This page from the Psalter contains part of Psalm 18 (National Library of Scotland, Adv. MS 72.1.4, f.1r).

Germany, which was the major supplier of jettons between the 1300s and the 1500s. The book would have been closed by winding a thong around the jetton. It is named a 'Psalter' because it contains both a compendium of basic medical definitions and also the doctor's alternative for the 'Divine Office', both of which were required for the health of the souls and bodies of his patients. As it was purchased from John Freebairn, the bookseller, in 1736 along with other manuscripts, the possibility is that it had also been in the possession of Rev. John Beaton.

## Calendar and Medical Manuscript, Poems, Charms and Folk Cures

This manuscript (NLS, Adv. MS 72. 1. 33) is written by a number of hands, including several Beatons and an Ó Conchubhair (another family of Irish physicians). It consists of a poem on the calendar usually attributed to Seán Ó Dubhagáin, followed by various

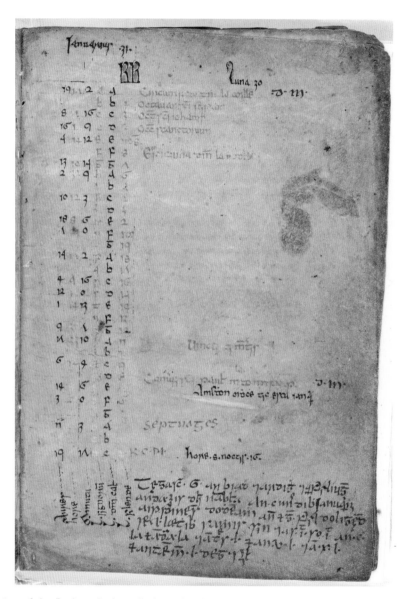

The beginning of the Psalter deals with the calendar, this page showing the month of January. Scholars have deduced that the year referred to is 1538. The columns are labelled *Aures, Hore, Minuta, L. signorum, L. dom. cal.* and *L. kalende.* The insertion of feast days and extra notes would have been added at different times by different writers (National Library of Scotland, Adv. MS 72.1.33, f.3r).

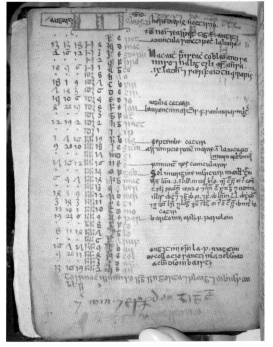
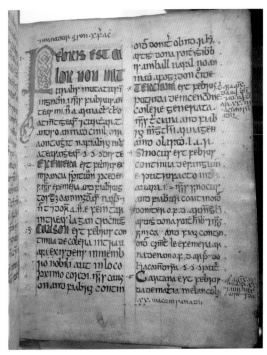

Left, a page from the calendar for the month of August. It gives the names of saints under their respective 'days' with numerous astrological and medical notes (La.III.21.f.11). Right, a page of carefully executed script, with ornamental lettering (La.III.21.f 44).

medical texts, with the addition of some charms and folk cures.

The second section is written on paper and consists of various medical texts written by a number of recognisable hands, including those of Donald, Neil, Malcolm, James and the Rev. John Beaton.

Between two pages in this manuscript was found a letter written sometime between 1593 and 1596 from Lachlan Mór, 14th Maclean of Duart, to Malcolm Beaton, his personal physician, which is considered to be of greater importance than any part of the manuscript proper, partly because it confirms Malcolm's succession as Ollamh Muileach.[114]

A translation of the letter, which was written in medieval Gaelic, reads:

A thousand blessings from Lachlan MacLean to his personal physician, Malcolm Beaton. He is asking you, on his own behalf and that of the Laird of Coll to visit MacCailean's [or maybe Argyll's] granddaughter and do what good you can for her. I am much obliged to you and send my blessings to the daughter of Iain Stewart and all her children. I am Lachlan MacLean.[115]

It appears that Lachlan Mór Maclean was writing this letter from Duart Castle, addressing it to Malcolm, his Ollamh Muileach, who was at that time in Appin, visiting the Stewart family, who were related by marriage to the Macleans. Further details of this letter can be found in Appendix 4.

## The Laing Manuscript, with the MacBeth (Beaton) Genealogy

This manuscript (La. III.21) was part of the collection compiled by David Laing, a bookseller and collector in Edinburgh, during the 1800s, which is why it is referred to as 'The Laing Manuscript'. The entire Laing Collection is held by Edinburgh University Library Special Collections.[116] Donald MacKinnon, who was Professor of Celtic

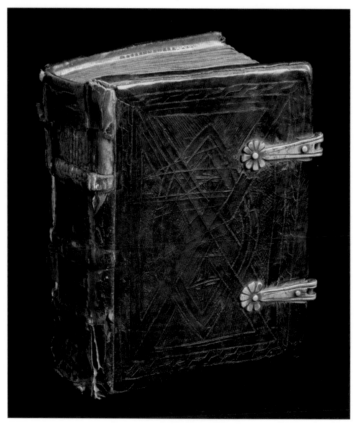

The binding of the Laing Manuscript (Edinburgh University Library, La III.21).

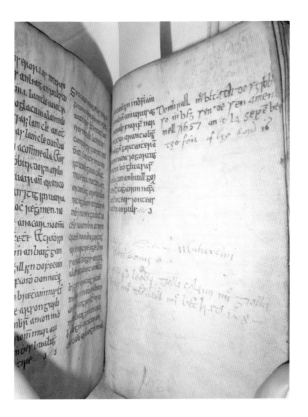

The earliest date, 1587, which occurs in the manuscript follows the entry written by Malcolm McBeath, thought to be one of the Pennycross physicians commemorated on the Beaton Cross (La.III.21.f.156r).

Medicine at Edinburgh University in the early twentieth century made a study of this and many other Gaelic manuscripts, and his research suggests that this manuscript dates from the early sixteenth century.[117] Apart from the original text, the earliest entry was written by one of the Pennycross Beatons, is dated 1587, and reads, '*Is se so leobhar Giolla Colaim Mic Giolla Enndris Mic Domhnaill Mic Bhethath*', meaning 'This is the book of Malcolm son of Gillanders son of Donald M'Beath'.

The Laing Manuscript is a medical volume and originally belonged to Fergus Beaton of Ballenabe, Islay, not arriving in the Beaton Library until some years later. It is a small book measuring 6 x 4½ inches and made from wooden boards, stoutly bound in skin and painted black. It is fastened with two silver clasps, one of which is broken. As with other similar manuscripts, various spaces were left blank in the original text, to be filled in later by different hands, correcting and supplementing the original as further experience and knowledge required. This, together with the size, covering and fastenings all suggest that it was also compiled as a *vade mecum* and is mostly written in Gaelic and Latin.

The first few pages of the book are taken up with a calendar and astrological table accompanied by numerous medical notes. These indicated which foods and drinks could be consumed in certain months and which should be avoided; times when it was safe to be bled, also days when it was lucky to buy land or enter a new house.

The rest of the manuscript is then concerned with various medical issues. However, the subject which receives most detailed treatment is urine, on which the writer dwells at great length, entering into minute detail regarding the various colours of urine as indicative of the nature of specific ailments. This part of the manuscript has been written with

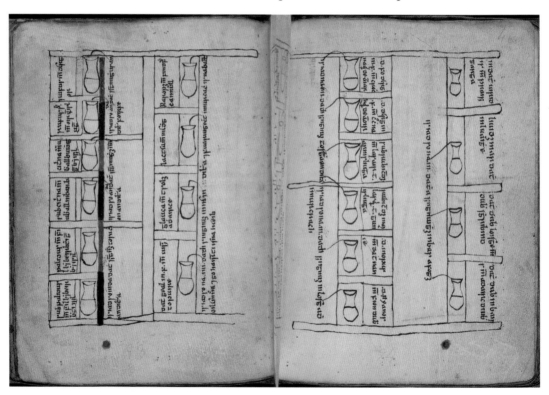

These pages show flasks containing urine, with careful descriptions of the colour, said to reveal the nature of an ailment (La. III. 21. ff.93-94).

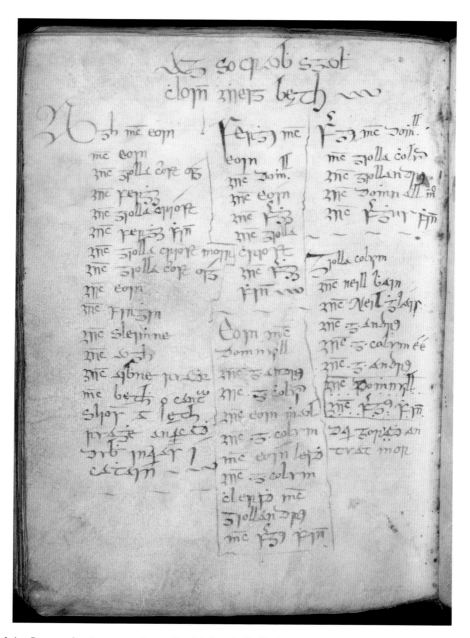

Part of the Beaton family tree – *Ag so Craobh Sgaoladh Choloinn Mheig Beth*, The Branches of the Clan MacBeth Here (La. III.21.f.102v).

great care, with large, ornamented or coloured initial letters. Although the handwriting varies, it is always clear and often very fine. Towards the end of the manuscript, the material was added at a much later date, is described as being 'miscellaneous' and was written in far less stylish hands, with several pages being written in the Scottish language.

Perhaps the main interest for scholars in this manuscript are the pedigrees or genealogical lists it contains. They were written by Christopher Beaton (McVeagh) of North Uist *c.*1670 and trace six separate branches of the Beaton family known to the author, back to a common ancestor, Fergus Fionn, whose forefathers originated in Ireland. There may well, of course, have been other families that were unknown to Christopher. Although he did not say where any of the six families were located, scholars have recognised one of the lists as that of the Pennycross family. These names appear at the top of the third column.

| | |
|---|---|
| Ferghus Mac Domh[nai]ll | Fergus son of Donald |
| Mhic Giolla Cholum | Son of Malcolm |
| Mhic Giollandrus | Son of Gillanders (Andrew) |
| Mhic Domhna[i]ll mhoir | Son of Donald great |
| Mhic Ferghus fhinn | Son of Fergus fair |

The first note on the second page reads: '*De his rebus satis dictum et scriptum per me Christopherus McVeagh*' meaning, 'Enough has been said and written regarding these matters by me, Christopher McBeth'.

The second note below the list of names reads: '*Hic liber est Fergusii McVeagh habitantis Peanagross*'. 'This book belongs to Fergus McBeth, who lives at Pennycross'.

## What Has Been Lost

It is clear that the 'Beaton Library' originally contained more than the 25 volumes that still remain.

What is also clear is that we are fortunate to have even that number of surviving texts, considering the time involved, the fact that they were in constant use, carried around the countryside and exposed to all sorts of climatic conditions, not to mention warfare, neglect and ignorance of their value.

In the *First Statistical Account for the parishes of Kilfinichen and Kilvickeon* of 1795, the writer, Rev. Dugald Campbell, spoke of the Beatons and of one of their manuscripts: 'They had a large folio MS. in Gaelic, treating of physic, which was left with a woman, the heiress of the Beatons, and seen by some now living; but what became of it, the incumbent, after all his inquiries, could not find. It is perhaps lost, as the heirs of this woman are quite illiterate.'[118] We must be grateful that this was not the fate of more of the manuscripts.

It has only been possible in this book to look at a very small number of these manuscripts, and for those readers who are

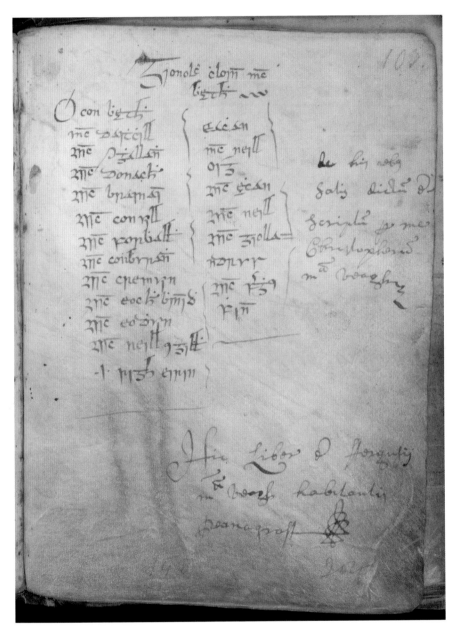

The remainder of Beaton family tree, listed with notes added by Christopher McVeagh/McBeth, the writer, and Fergus McVeagh/Beaton who kept the book as part of the Beaton Library (La. III.21.f.103r).

interested in seeing individual pages in detail, as well as discovering more about their contents, the website 'Irish Script on Screen', *https://www.isos.dias.ie/collection/nls.html*, has a large collection of images from the Scottish National Library collection and contains much of the research done by Ronald Black.

## The Beaton Physic Garden in the Twenty-first Century

As has already been mentioned, local children who grew up in the Pennyghael and Pennycross area between the two World Wars remembered being told by parents not to eat anything that came from this area, as they didn't know what was still growing there. Thus the 'legend' of the garden was still alive as late as the early twentieth century. Given this fear of the unknown, it seems likely that once the

garden had finally gone out of use, it would not have been used for anything more than grazing cattle, until a time when the 'old stories' were no longer handed down. In winter, when the rampant bracken growth has collapsed, the outline of the surrounding stone dyke is clearly visible. Along the north side of the garden are remains of a line of ancient trees. When Mary Beith (author of *Healing Threads*) visited the Garden in the 1990s, she suggested that the remaining trees in that area had been a deliberate planting.

In March 2023, an archaeological walk-over survey was undertaken by Dr Clare Ellis on what is believed to be the remains of the Physic Garden. A substantial sub-rectangular stone enclosure was mapped, along with the probable remains of a dwelling, two stone quarries and the remains of other stone walls of a former designed landscape.

Left, a section of the enclosure wall which is still visible at the north end of the garden. It is likely that over the centuries, all the useful stones from the site have been removed and recycled. Right, a possible entrance into the Physic Garden in the north-west corner (photos by C. Ellis).

A bracken-covered mound thought to be the site of a building corresponding with the position of a house shown on the Langlands map. It is quite possible that this is the site of the Beaton house, but it is unlikely that even excavation would prove this (photo by Miek Zwamborn).

The possible garden enclosure comprises a substantial stone wall some 1.10m wide, which is constructed from large blocks of basalt that form the inner and outer faces with a coarse rubble core; the wall only survives to a height of 0.43m. The enclosure is sub-rectangular in form, with a probable entrance on the north side near the west corner. The entrance appears to have been carved through a natural basalt outcrop which forms the northern boundary of the garden enclosure.

A dwelling is depicted on Langland's map of 1819 and a house platform is clearly visible at this location measuring some 14-15m x 4m wide. At the north-west end a low bank hints at the survival of a wall, although apart from one stray stone there is no surviving masonry. It is entirely possible that the stone has been robbed or cleared from the site.

During the same month in 2023 John Clare, an ecologist, conducted a survey of the belt of trees at the northern boundary of the garden enclosure, thought to have been established as a shelter belt. While there are several trees of interest here, one of the most interesting is the huge multi-limbed sessile oak, which still dominates the area. This tree

Above, the ancient sessile oak which still dominates the belt of trees at the north end of the garden, in summer . . . and below, in winter (photos by Christine Leach).

was coppiced and then partially collapsed many years in the past. Despite this it is in a very healthy condition. The base of this oak is about 4 metres wide, giving an approximate girth of 8 to 9 metres, indicating that it is an extremely ancient specimen.

Further details of both these surveys can be found in Appendix 6.

# 6

# *Create Your Own Beaton Garden*

## A Garden of Herbs

(Photos by Elizabeth Carter)

Follow in the footsteps of the Beatons of Pennycross by creating your own Physic Garden with a selection of tasty herbs and a lovely array of bee-friendly, flowering plants. Connect your own garden with that of your ancestors and a period of time extending from 1572 to the 1650s, a time which includes the birth of Shakespeare, Oliver Cromwell leading an army into Edinburgh, Sir Francis Drake and the Spanish Armada and the beheading of Mary Queen of Scots. This viewpoint offers another way of looking at plants in the light of the ancient wisdom of herbal medicine employed by the physicians of the past. You may find you look at plants differently in the context of this history.

On the following pages is just a small selection of the many plants the Beaton physicians might have grown at Pennycross, with descriptions of past and present medical uses. The plants listed here are easy to source and grow; you can incorporate them into your existing garden by planting them in the ground or growing them in pots; or you might even want to create your own dedicated Beaton plot. All are safe to eat, unless otherwise stated, and all are currently available as herbal supplements.

Please note: the modern medicinal herbal uses listed here are not comprehensive, as plants have many healing qualities.

**Importantly, always seek professional advice before using plants as medicines**.

## General planting guidelines

Water plants on the soil at the roots. Getting the leaves and flowers wet when the roots are dry increases the chance of mildew.

It is a good idea to wear gloves when handling plants, to avoid irritation from leaves and stems.

Cut back after flowering if you would like to tidy up the plant, hope for a second flowering in the current season, or to reduce self-seeding.

Flowering times and height may vary, depending where grown, climate and soil conditions.

## BAY LAUREL

### Latin: *Laurus nobilis*; Gaelic: *an laibhreis*

Bay leaves were used to make the traditional laurel wreaths and garlands in ancient Greece and Rome worn by emperors, victorious athletes, heroes and poets. (Today, winners of Grand Prix races are still bedecked with laurel wreaths.) Bay was grown as a decorative evergreen tree, and Henry VIII, at the time of the dissolution of the monasteries, seized three loads of bay trees from the gardens of the Carthusian monastery of Charterhouse in London, to replant in his own garden at Hampton Court. As a strewing herb, bay leaves were commonly sprinkled on the floors to mask odours and to keep moths away, owing to the leaf's lauric acid content, which gives it insecticidal properties.

**Medicinal:** The herb was used for headaches and migraines and to keep the plague at bay.

**Culinary:** The leaves would be dried and added flavour to soups and stews. At a Tudor banquet, a boar's head would be served wrapped in bay leaves, with sprigs of rosemary in its ears and a roasted pippin (apple) stuffed in its open mouth. Fresh leaves were also used but, for many, the taste of these was too bitter.

**Magic and myth:** Bay leaves were used for centuries in witch spells for protection and to prevent a person from being cheated, tricked or harmed by someone with ill intentions. They were also used in spells to protect people from the plague.

Bay Laurel.

**Modern uses:** Bay laurel is mostly used as a pain remedy for migraine and for ailments related to the upper part of the digestive tract.

**Flowers:** Late spring to early summer.

**Height:** Up to 152cm (60in). An evergreen shrub, it prefers partial shade or sun and is good to grow in a pot in a sheltered position. Younger plants can be susceptible to frost damage.

## BETONY

### Latin: *Betonica officinalis*; Gaelic: *Lus Beathaig*

Also known as Common Hedgenettle, Bishopwort and Wood Betony, it was once an

Betony.

incredibly popular herb; its fame was great and and it was highly valued throughout the Middle Ages. In Mary Beith's book, *The Healing Threads*, her research records that betony only naturally grew in the far south of Scotland. As it was so popular a herb in Gaelic medicine, it may well have been grown specifically in medicinal gardens in more northerly areas. Scots Gaelic also has the name for it of *Glasair-coille*, which translates as 'green one of the wood'.

**Medicinal:** Whether drunk or eaten, it was used for curing everything you can think of, including afflictions of the eyes, heart, lungs, stomach, bowels, kidneys and spleen. It was also recommended for headaches and migraine, hysterics and nervous afflictions, for fresh head wounds, for stimulating the appetite, treating paralysis and epilepsy, reducing fever and violent chills, healing carbuncles, curing jaundice and lightening a leaden complexion. Betony juice was dropped into the ear to help restore lost hearing.

**Culinary:** Dried leaves and flowers made a herbal tea and fresh leaves were used in salads.

**Magic and myth:** Betony's fame was so great that the home in which it was planted was believed to be safe from all dangers. Johann Petri's *Herbarius Latinus* (1484) speaks of its magical aspects as 'having the power to reveal all that is malicious and deadly'. It could be drunk as a tea or its leaves worn around the neck to prevent nocturnal visitations, terrifying dreams, visions, sleepwalking and nightmares. Hildegard de Bingen's *Causes and Cures* (*c.*1151) considered it to be 'particularly efficacious in countering love spells of a diabolic origin', and stipulated that to break the spell, the bewitched party, whether male or female, must seek out betony that has not yet been used for either a medicinal or a magical purpose.

**Modern uses:** Leaves and flowers are used, fresh or dried, to treat a wide range of complaints, including anxiety, gallstones, heartburn, high blood pressure, migraine and neuralgia, and to prevent sweating. Externally, leaves can be made into an ointment or applied direct to cuts and sores.

**Flowers:** July to September.

**Height:** Up to 60cm (24in). A perennial, it prefers full sun or partial shade.

## BORAGE

**Latin:** *Borago officinalis*; **Gaelic:** *Borrach*

Also known as Starflower, it was referred to as the herb of courage and its name may be derived from the Celtic word *borrach*, meaning 'glad courage'. Borage tea was thought to promote bravery before battle and the wielding of a sword.

**Medicinal:** Borage is good for bronchial, chest and other respiratory complaints, stomach problems and to expel poisons of all kinds. In medieval times the leaves and flowers would make a poultice for swellings and it was used

Borage.

as a tonic to lift the heart and spirit. Pliny the Elder (77 AD), and later the Elizabethan herbalist, John Gerard, have all mentioned the marvellous effects of the plant on mind and body for dispelling melancholy and inducing euphoria, and it was added to wine 'for strengthening the heart'. The *Regimen Sanitatis* advised people convalescing from bloodletting to eat borage, it being rich in vitamins.

**Culinary:** Young leaves were used as a fresh vegetable or a dried herb and added a cucumber-like flavour to salads and drinks. The pretty blue flowers were used as a garnish.

**Modern uses:** Borage is widely available as an oil, capsules, or herbal tea, and used to treat a variety of respiratory and digestive disorders, to help regulate the body's immune system, and fight joint inflammation.

**Flowers:** June to July.

**Height:** Up to 90cm (36in). As it is an annual plant, sow seeds outside in spring, late summer or autumn when the ground is warm. Grow in full sun or partial shade. Avoid the roots drying out in the summer and be careful with handling the hairy stems and leaves, as they can be a skin irritant.

## (ROMAN) CHAMOMILE

**Latin:** *Anthemis nobile*; **Gaelic:** *Cama-mhil*

Associated with St Anne, mother of the Virgin Mary, it was one of the nine sacred Anglo-Saxon herbs. Its oil was used to perfume baths and

Chamomile.

**Magic and myth:** A component in medieval love potions to attract love, it was also used to prevent nightmares.

**Modern uses:** As a sedative, chamomile tea can aid sleep and reduce anxiety, while its anti-inflammatory qualities are used to relieve joint inflammation. It is also used topically to soothe inflamed or irritated skin.

**Flowers:** June to October.

**Height:** Up to 30cm (12in). A perennial, it can be grown in full sun, as it is drought resistant.

## COMFREY

**Latin:** *Symphytum officinale*;
**Gaelic:** *Meacan dubh* **or** *Lus nan cnàmh briste*

With China as its country of origin, comfrey was traded throughout Asia and Europe via the Silk Road from Roman times.

**Medicinal:** Comfrey was also known as Boneset or Knitbone, due to its ability to knit together tissues and promote cell growth. The young leaves were boiled to make a poultice which was wrapped around broken bones, bruises and sprains. The Gaelic name translates as 'plant for broken bones'. A hot infusion of comfrey leaves brought relief to symptoms of the common cold by stimulating resistance to viral and bacterial infections, loosening phlegm and reducing fever by encouraging sweating. With a tonic and laxative effect, it was also used for internal haemorrhaging,

the gentle aroma of its leaves, when crushed, made it a popular strewing herb.

**Medicinal:** Chamomile helped with digestion and was used as a liver tonic. Culpeper's *Complete Herbal* (1653) stated that 'it easeth all pains of the cholic and stone, and all pains and torments of the belly'. With anti-inflammatory and antimicrobial properties, it has also been used since ancient times to treat wounds and for fighting bacterial and fungal infections. Cramps could be alleviated by rubbing in an ointment made from chamomile mixed with butter. As a sedative, it was good for headaches. Chamomile tea, infused with the plants dittany of Crete, scabious and pennyroyal, was a preferred medieval remedy against poison and also known for its soothing and relaxing properties.

**Culinary:** Chamomile was used as a tea and to flavour beer.

Comfrey.

rickets, dysentery, diseases of the bladder and the kidneys, rheumatic illness, worms, and skin conditions such as sores and eczema.

**Culinary:** Young leaves were used as a substitute for asparagus, or added raw to a medieval salad.

**Modern uses:** Such was the reputation of this herb for its ability to speed up healing in wounds and bones, that comfrey tablets were standard issue in World War Two First Aid packs. Comfrey is said to have a variety of healing properties, is predominantly applied topically, and is available as an ointment, salve and herbal tincture.

**Flowers:** June to October.

**Height:** Up to 150cm (60in). A perennial, it will grow in full sun or partial shade but can

be invasive. Wear gloves when handling, as the little hairs covering the stems can irritate the skin.

## CYCLAMEN, WILD, IVY-LEAVED

### Latin: *Cyclamen hederifolium*; Gaelic: *Cularan*

Cyclamen comes from the Latin word *cyclaminos* and the Greek word *kýklos* which means 'circle' or 'wheel' and refers to the shape of the plant's tubers. Other names include Alpine Violet, Persian Violet, and Sowbread, the last name being because pigs liked to dig and eat the tubers and were immune to the toxicity of the plant. The Gaelic name *cularan* means 'boar's bread'. Pliny the Elder (23-79 AD) stated in his writings that the plant was

Cyclamen.

used as a poison and applied to arrows in ancient Rome.

**Medicinal:** Despite its dangerous side-effects, cyclamen was once recommended as a remedy for a variety of ailments including eye disease, gout, snakebite, tinnitus, menstrual pains, skin rashes and as a powerful laxative. A poultice made from bruised tubers would be applied to help indolent ulcers while the juice was a treatment for vertigo. It is a plant that was well known to herbalists and physicians, including Pedanius Dioscorides (first century AD) and later Nicholas Culpeper, who also believed it could be used to accelerate birth, promote expulsion of the afterbirth and to induce menstruation.

**Culinary: Not edible (and can be toxic to cats and dogs).**

**Modern uses:** For a blocked nose and sinusitis, a homeopathic remedy is made from the fresh root. It is applied externally to the bowels to cause purging.

**Flowers:** Autumn and winter.

**Height:** 10cm (4in) It is a perennial and the tubers should be planted in partial shade.

## FENNEL

### Latin: *Foeniculum vulgare*;
### Gaelic: *Luș an t-saoidh*

Fennel was cultivated by the ancient Romans for its aromatic fruits and succulent, edible shoots. The smell of the plant was thought to

Fennel.

resemble that of hay, and *foeniculum* is derived from the Latin word *foenum*, meaning 'hay'. It was a popular herb in the household of King Edward I of England, with his account books from 1281 listing 'a purchase of 8$\frac{1}{2}$ pounds of fennel seed' (a month's supply). On Church-mandated *fastying dayes*, the faithful used fennel to get through the fast. They would bring handkerchiefs with fennel seed to nibble on during long services to stave off hunger.

**Medicinal:** Esteemed by many herbalists for its peculiarly strengthening effect on the sight due to its antioxidants, it was used to treat eye inflammation and failing eyesight. Pliny, in his *Naturalis Historia* (77 AD), believed so much in the power of fennel that he used it to treat 22 different ailments, observing also that serpents 'cast off their old skins, and they sharpen their sight with the juice by rubbing against the plant'. The seeds were chewed to sweeten breath, help treat a toothache, and gargled to relieve sore throats. It was also used to treat colds, fevers, insanity, stomach and heart ailments, infant colic and body odour, the leaves being chewed to help with digestive problems. When steeped into a tea it was believed that fennel was also a treatment for losing weight as it works as an appetite suppressant. Fennel was believed to be an effective antidote for poisonous mushrooms and snakebite, and a plaster of fennel roots was a traditional treatment for the bites of mad dogs. The Beatons mention prescribing it for increasing the flow of urine.

**Culinary:** Fennel was often used when cooking fish and to flavour salads and soups. The seed was used as a condiment, especially for salt fish.

**Magic and myth:** During medieval times, fennel was hung over doorways and its seeds inserted into keyholes to protect a dwelling and its inhabitants from evil spirits and witches, particularly around Midsummer's Eve, when they were thought to roam freely.

**Modern uses:** For the relief of constipation and bloating, digestion, PMS and menstrual cramps, menopause, and to help detoxify and cleanse the liver.

**Flowers:** Early summer.

**Height:** Up to 180cm (70in). A perennial, it should be sown outside in the spring when the ground is warm. It prefers full sun or partial shade, a sheltered position and moist soil.

## FEVERFEW

### Latin: *Tanacetum parthenium*; Gaelic: *Meadh-duach*

A corruption of the Latin word *febrifugia* meaning 'something that drives away fevers'. The leaves were also used as a moth repellent.

**Medicinal:** When it was brought to Britain by medieval herbalists, the leaves, fresh or dried, were used to reduce fevers and relieve headaches and migraine. The plant was also

Feverfew.

known for treating toothache, arthritis and melancholy. Culpeper's *Complete Herbal* stated 'It is very effectual for all pains in the head coming of a cold cause, the herb being bruised and applied to the crown of the head: as also for the vertigo; that is, a running or swimming of the head.'

**Culinary:** The flowers were dried and used for a herbal tea.

**Modern uses:** It is mainly used for the relief of headaches and migraine.

**Flowers:** June to September.

**Height:** Up to 45cm (18in). A perennial, it prefers full sun and should be sown outside in the spring when the ground is warm.

# FOXGLOVE

### Latin: *Digitalis purpurea*;
### Gaelic: *Lus nam ban-sìth*

The Latin name *Digitalis* comes from *digitanus*, meaning 'finger', possibly because a finger could fit inside the thimble-shaped flowers. Foxglove is an ancient name that goes back at least to the early fourteenth century and it has many other names including Witch's Gloves, Bloody Bells and Fairy Thimbles. The Gaelic means 'fairy women's plant'. It was also called Cow-flop and Dead Man's Bells, perhaps to indicate the plant's poisonous qualities. In Christian traditions, the plant is associated with the Virgin Mary and called Our Lady's Gloves.

Foxglove.

**Medicinal:** It was used (with care) to treat heart problems, the kidneys and various urinary conditions, abscesses, boils, headaches, paralysis, stomach ulcers and open wounds. Bruising the leaves and binding them around old sores would help to cleanse, dry and heal them. However, overdosing could result in vomiting, diarrhoea, delirium and death. Early physicians developed the Doctrine of Signatures – a system that believed in the principle that God gave plants a certain appearance to show mankind what part of the body it could medicinally treat. With foxglove therefore, they thought the flowers looked like an animal's open mouth and the speckles in the mouth of the flower were seen as symbolic of inflammation of the throat, so this meant it must have some medicinal value in the treatment of injuries of the mouth and throat.

**Culinary:** Not edible as all parts of the plant are poisonous.

**Magic and myth:** The name foxglove could be

derived from Folks Glove meaning the gloves of 'The Folk', who, to our fourteenth-century ancestors, were the fairies. There is a legend which says that the fairies gave the flower to foxes to wear in order to muffle their footsteps when being hunted. It may also have come from the Anglo-Saxon word *foxes-gleow* meaning 'a ring of bells', their sound being a spell of protection against hunters and hounds. A medieval potion made from foxglove was said to be able to 'break a faery spell' and 'restore changelings to true children'. Medieval witches used this plant for creating death potions.

**Modern uses:** It has long been used (and continues to be) to treat heart conditions.

**Flowers:** June to September.

**Height:** Up to 150cm (60in). Some plants will flower for several years but generally it is a biennial and is happy in sun or partial shade. All parts of this plant are toxic to humans, so should be handled with care and while wearing gloves.

## HEARTSEASE

### Latin: *Viola tricolor*;
### Gaelic: *Goirmean-searradh*

The cheerful little blooms of heartsease can appear in a variety of colours. Other names include Johnny-jump-up, Wild pansy and Love-lies-bleeding, the plant being associated with the love of Christ. Early Christians saw the

Heartsease.

three-coloured petals as a symbol of the Holy Trinity, while King Arthur and his knights at the Round Table believed the lines on the petals foretold their future. Heartsease features as a love-charm in Shakespeare's *Midsummer Night's Dream*: 'The juice of it, on sleeping eyelids laid, will make or man or woman madly dote upon the next live creature that it sees.'

**Medicinal:** As it was a good blood purifier, infusions of the flowers had many uses, including pain relief, treatment of lung inflammation, epilepsy, eczema and other skin diseases. It was made into a syrup to treat coughs and fevers and Culpeper thought it 'excellently good for the convulsions in children, as also for the falling sickness'. The early physicians, guided by the Doctrine of Signatures, thought the upper portion of heartsease flowers resembled the upper lobes of the heart, and so it was used for all problems related to the heart.

**Culinary:** Young buds and leaves were used in soup, and the flowers in salads.

**Magic and myth:** Heartsease is rich in folklore and was associated with love in both Roman and Greek mythology. In medieval times, the plant was used for its potency in love charms.

**Modern uses:** Heartsease flowers can be applied to blisters, pimples, acne, eczema, wounds and other skin conditions. A herbal tea is brewed from the flowers and can be taken as a tonic and to treat some respiratory conditions.

**Flowers:** April to September.

**Height:** 12cm (5in). As it is an annual plant, sow seeds outside in spring, late summer or early autumn in sun or partial shade.

## LADY'S MANTLE

**Latin:** *Alchemilla vulgaris*;
**Gaelic:** *Copan an driùchd*

The family name *Alchemilla* stems from the word *alchemy*, and refers to the belief in medieval times that water droplets forming on, and magically held by, its leaves could turn base metals to gold and could also be used in regaining youth. The Gaelic name means 'dew cup', which is an apt description. The leaves' scalloped edges are reputed to have given the plant its name due to the resemblance to a woman's cloak. It was used as a strewing herb.

**Medicinal:** Lady's Mantle was chiefly a herb for women's ailments, both when taken

Lady's Mantle.

internally and externally applied. Its anti-inflammatory and analgesic properties were thought to be good for reducing pain associated with menstruation, to help conception and to overcome 'flagging breasts'. A preparation of dried leaves was used to control diarrhoea. As an antiseptic, and to stop bleeding, it was widely used as an ointment or poultice for the treatment of sores and wounds.

**Culinary:** The leaves were used as a herbal tea for its soothing properties.

**Magic and myth:** It was also known as Elf-shot and seen as a powerful remedy for healing an animal which had been shot by a malevolent elf.

**Modern uses:** It is used for easing menopausal symptoms, period pains, PMS and to help regulate menstruation, also to improve skin health and promote sleep.

**Flowers:** June to August.

**Height:** Up to 45cm (18in). A perennial, it is to be grown in full sun or partial shade.

## MALLOW

**Latin:** *Malva sylvestris*;
**Gaelic:** *Ucas fiadhain*

Mallow has a rich ethnomedicinal history and has been used since ancient Greek and Roman times.

**Medicinal:** The whole plant was used, but the root was most valued and used as a purgative, to get out thorns and splinters and to treat distemper. The upper side of a leaf would be laid

Mallow.

on a wound or sore to induce suppuration, or made into a poultice to treat hard tumours, inflammations and swellings. It was a treatment for headache and catarrh, and it was recommended to be eaten after bloodletting. Mallow tea, sweetened with a syrup of violets, was a purgative cure for cystitis.

**Culinary:** The leaves and shoots of common mallow have been used as food sources since the eighth century BC. The leaves can be cooked and eaten like spinach or added to soups to thicken them. The flowers and buds can be pickled.

**Modern uses:** Leaves and flowers collected in summer and boiled in water are used against a dry cough and to relieve inflammation of the throat, pharynx and larynx. It is also widely used as a mild laxative and to treat haemorrhoids.

**Flowers:** June to October.

**Height:** 150cm (60in). A perennial, it prefers a sheltered position in full sun.

## MUGWORT

**Latin:** *Artemisia vulgaris*; **Gaelic:** *Liath-lus*

The Gaelic means 'grey weed'. Its bitter qualities made it useful as a strewing plant and to repel moths. The stalk tops preceded the use of hops in the brewing of beer and it was dried and smoked before tobacco became popular.

**Medicinal:** Mugwort was believed to have many medicinal properties and was thought

Mugwort.

aid for prophecy and was reputed to prevent weariness on a journey.

**Modern uses:** Mugwort is used to promote menstruation, and treat stomach disorders, including stimulating the appetite, easing nausea or curing worms.

**Flowers:** July to September.

**Height:** Up to 150cm (60in). A perennial, it prefers sunny conditions or partial shade. Remove flower heads before the seeds set, as this is a prolific self-seeder.

## PARSLEY

**Latin:** *Petroselinum sativum*; **Gaelic:** *Pearsal*

*Petroselinum* comes from the Latin *petrosus* meaning 'stony', because 'it grows in or near stones and stony places'. This perhaps was taken from the fact that it could be grown in poorer soil. In ancient Rome it was associated with the goddess Persephone, queen of the underworld, and was used in funeral ceremonies. During the Dark Ages, Christians in Europe were forbidden to transplant parsley, in the belief that doing so invited death and crop failure. Mention of parsley in Britain goes back to the mid-1300s, where it was regularly grown in herb and infirmary gardens as well as kitchen gardens.

**Medicinal:** Chewing parsley was thought to relieve intestinal gas, increase urine flow and to act as a mild laxative. It was also used for coughs, to treat bruises, and to counteract the

to be effective against poisons and fevers; useful as a sedative; for removing parasites; for foot problems (it was made into a foot ointment); for stress, asthma, epilepsy and for hastening and easing labour and childbirth. Its bitter taste was an appetite stimulant, and thought to strengthen the stomach.

**Culinary:** Young shoots, flower buds, flowers, stems and leaves were all used as a potherb and for flavouring poultry, stuffing and dumplings, and the leaves or shoots were cooked as a vegetable.

**Magic and myth:** This herb has been used in magical ceremonies the world over since before recorded history, and was one of the most popular herbs in Anglo-Saxon magic. Keeping mugwort in one's house prevented wicked ghosts and spirits from living there, it was an effects of poisons and snakebite. It was a calming and soothing herb for the nervous system. It was used to treat eye inflammations, Culpeper's *Complete Herbal* saying 'Leaves laid to the eyes inflamed with heat, or swollen, helps them'. Crushed parsley seeds were used against parasites, as they were thought able to get rid of head and body lice.

**Culinary:** Parsley was regularly used in cooking, added to pottages and casseroles, chopped in salads, and added to sauces to make them a rich green colour. It is included in recipes in the *The Forme of Cury*, the oldest known English language instructive cookery book (*c.*1390) detailing over 200 recipes and written by the Master-Cooks of King Richard II. (The Middle-English word cury means cookery.)

Parsley.

**Magic and myth:** The Romans did not eat parsley, however they wore wreaths of it around their heads during feasts to keep drunkenness away. In British folklore it was thought that giving parsley away would bring bad luck.

**Modern uses:** As a digestive aid, parsley can be made into a herbal tea to be consumed before meal times.

**Flowers:** June.

**Height:** Up to 60cm (24in). A biennial, it is best to grow parsley in sun or partial shade.

## PENNYROYAL

### Latin: *Mentha pulegium*;
### Gaelic: *A'pheighinn rìoghail*

Greek mythology and the *Mentha* (Mint) family are said to be connected. Minthe was a river nymph in the Cocytus River (one of the five rivers of Hades). Persephone caught her husband Hades as he was about to seduce her, and to take her revenge she turned Minthe into a lowly mint plant that people would walk upon. Mint supposedly got its pungent sweet smell when Hades softened the spell so that when people walked upon his lover they would smell her sweetness. It was also known as fleabane because, when rubbed on the skin or strewn, pennyroyal was able to repel fleas and rodents.

**Medicinal:** Pennyroyal was a digestive tonic and cough remedy, it purified stale drinking water and was a preferred medieval remedy

Pennyroyal.

against poison. Culpeper's *Complete Herbal* suggests it be used to reduce nausea and states that it 'purges melancholy' When mixed with bramble root, infusions treated bronchitis and asthma.

**Culinary:** With its strong flavour, it was used sparingly as flavouring in salads and cooked foods. Pennyroyal is rarely used as such today, as its flavour is considered far too strong for our palates. However, the leaves may be infused in hot water to make a strong mint tea.

**Modern uses:** It is mainly available as a herbal tea for digestive or respiratory problems.

**Flowers:** July to September.

**Height:** 23cm (9in). This perennial grows best in partial shade.

# PRIMROSE

## Latin: *Primula vulgaris*; Gaelic: *Sòbhrach*

The primrose has long been associated with birth, marriage and death. Common names include Golden Rose, Lent Rose, Easter Rose, and Butter Rose. The name comes from *prima rosa*, meaning 'first rose' in medieval Latin, as it is one of the first flowers to appear in the spring. The Romans held that primroses were given to the earth in memory of a son of the goddess Flora, while Celtic peoples believed the flower to be sacred, representing renewal and the return of abundance. The flower's original association with Brigid, the goddess of rebirth, was modified in Christian times by linking it with St Bride, with bunches of primroses being offered to her on the first day of February (also the date of the pagan festival *Imbolc*). In medieval times, the flower was dedicated to St Agatha, and was ceremonially gathered by children on 13 March. In later

Primrose.

Christian legend it was dedicated to St Valentine. Chaucer's poem *Parliament of Fowls* contains the first reference to Valentine's Day as being a romantic occasion, and there was a medieval Valentine's saying: 'If you see a bluebird you will marry a happy person; if you see a goldfinch you will marry a rich person; if you see a sparrow you will marry a poor person; if you find a glove your future beloved will have the other one.'[119] The primrose is also associated with the story of Melicerta, whose lover pined away after her sudden death, while Shakespeare associates the plant with death, referring to it as the funeral flower for youth in Act 4 of *Cymbeline*.

**Medicinal:** An astringent and sedative, it was prescribed for a wide variety of ailments, including skin lesions, headaches, coughs, rheumatism, fever, spasms, cramps and paralysis, and was also added to wine as a cure for palsy. John Gerard, in his book *The Herball* (1597), stated that 'Primrose tea drunk in the month of May is famous for curing the phrenzies'. A hundred years later, Culpeper in his *Complete Herbal* was of the opinion that, 'Of the leaves is made as fine a salve to heal wounds as any I know'.

**Culinary:** Young leaves, either raw or cooked as a potherb, were added to soups and stews, and its flowers made an attractive garnish to salads. The leaves mixed with other herbs added flavour to stuffing for meat and poultry.

**Magic and myth:** The primrose was used as a love oracle, as it represented inconstancy and a lover's doubts. It was also associated with safety and posies of primroses were left on the doorstep to encourage fairies to bless a house and anyone living in it.

**Modern uses:** It is used as a salve for cuts, burns and other skin ailments, and in skin preparations to treat pimples and wrinkles. It can be an ingredient in soothing eyewashes, and an infusion of the roots is a good remedy against nervous headaches.

**Flowers:** March to June.

**Height:** 20cm (8in). This perennial grows best in partial shade.

## ROSEMARY

### Latin: *Rosmarinus officinalis*; Gaelic: *Ròs Muire*

Queen Philippa, wife of King Edward III, is believed to have introduced the herb to Britain from the Mediterranean in the fourteenth century when her mother sent her some cuttings. John Harvey, a twentieth-century authority on English medieval gardens, suggested that these cuttings were first planted in the privy garden of the old palace of Westminster. It would be interesting to know if the trainee physicians from Ireland brought rosemary back from their continental trips. Rosemary was a popular strewing plant, used to deter fleas and moths, and was burned as incense. There is a legend that describes Mary and

Rosemary.

**Magic and myth:** This herb was used as a symbol of love and faithfulness and burned as incense to prevent jealousy or infidelity. At weddings it was included in wreaths and garlands as a sign of love and loyalty, exchanged by brides and grooms instead of rings and presented as gifts to wedding guests. Among Celtic tribes also, rosemary was the symbol of fidelity with lovers. Putting the leaves under your pillow guarded against nightmares. Mothers hung twigs of rosemary above cradles to prevent fairies from carrying away the children and it was believed to ward off evil presences and protect homes.

**Modern uses:** The leaves and flowers are used in herbal teas, and its essential oils in aromatherapy. It is thought to promote eye health, and also to relieve headaches, colic, colds and depression, and to help boost the appetite.

**Flowers**: March to May.

**Height**: Up to 100cm (40in). Grow this small evergreen shrub in full sun and trim after flowering.

Joseph on their flight into Egypt, and Mary hanging Jesus' clothes on a rosemary bush to dry. The next day as they left, she blessed the plant, and its plain white flowers turned to a pretty pale blue and it developed a sweet scent in her honour.

**Medicinal:** Ancient practitioners had long used rosemary as a tonic for strengthening memory and focusing thoughts, but it had multiple other uses including the treatment of sprains, fractures, nervousness, dizziness and hysteria. It was also burnt and then used for cleaning teeth. Throughout Europe during the Middle Ages, it was hung in a small cloth bag around the neck to ward off the plague.

**Culinary:** It adds flavour to soups and stews, jams, jellies, biscuits and cakes.

## SAGE

**Latin:** *Salvia officinalis;* **Gaelic:** *Athair liath*

Thought to have been introduced to Britain by the Romans, sage's Latin name *Salvia* comes from *salvere*, meaning 'to heal', and its strong aroma made it popular as a strewing herb. The Gaelic name means 'grey father' or 'grey ancestor'.

**Medicinal:** Sage was known as a 'cure-all' and valued for centuries in this country for its antibacterial properties. It had many medicinal uses including for coughs, colds, night sweats, digestive problems, toothache, leprosy, worms and as an antiseptic. Richard Banckes' *Herball* (1525) stated 'It will make a man's body clean . . . it is a marvel that any inconvenience should grieve them that use it.' Also known as a tonic, it was thought to help calm the nerves and was recommended for use after bloodletting. Wild sage was used for worming horses and thought to help restore the eyesight of cows and sheep if it was placed in their ears.

**Culinary:** Used for stuffing duck and goose, pottage dishes and to flavour sausages and cheese, it was also highly valued in former times for making sage beer and sage tea.

Sage.

**Magic and myth**: It was known as a sacred herb, and many believed in the magic power of sage to protect people against evil. For centuries witches crushed sage into a special bowl and burned it, so the smoke would surround the person or fill the area that needed to be cleansed of negative energy. Later, these herbs were bundled together into sticks, known as smudge sticks, and then burned, a custom that continues to this day.

**Modern uses:** Fresh leaves infused to make a herbal tea are considered helpful in the relief of colds, flus and sore throats. It is also valued for its treatment of menopausal symptoms, such as hot flushes, and for its cleansing, purifying and deodorising properties in treating inflammatory conditions such as arthritis, gout or general inflammation of the cardiovascular system.

**Flowers:** July to September.

**Height:** 60cm (24in). Grow this small shrub, in full sun and prune in mid spring.

## ST JOHN'S WORT

**Latin:** *Hypericum perforatum*;
**Gaelic:** *Eala bhuidhe*

The common name is a reference to St John, the youngest of Jesus' twelve apostles. Its earliest use dates back to the sixth century when, according to Gaelic tradition, the missionary St Columba always carried a piece of St John's Wort because of his great regard for St

St John's Wort.

known that St John's Wort contains rutin, which affects the flow of adrenalin, in turn affecting the sympathetic nervous system. St John's Wort was also known to ease depression and anxiety and was good for bruises and burns. Culpeper's *Complete Herbal* said 'it is a singular wound herb, healing inward hurts or bruises', and as an ointment 'it opens obstructions, dissolves swelling and closes up the lips of wounds.' Jacob Meydenbach's *Hortus Sanitatis* (1491) recommends it be used to counteract poison from the thrusts of poisoned weapons.

John. The plant is sometimes alluded to as St Columba's Flower.

**Medicinal:** An alternative Gaelic name – *Achlasan Chalium-Chille* – the literal meaning of which is 'St Columba's oxterful', may come from the story of a young herdsman whose nerves were upset by long dark nights alone on the hillside with the cattle. He was brought to the saint to get a cure for his condition. Columba is said to have placed the St John's Wort in the boy's left armpit, whereupon he began to recover the balance of his mind. Mary Beith's *Healing Threads* suggests that this is so specific it may relate to poultices placed by healers in patients' armpits, an area of the body having numerous nerve-endings, glands and blood vessels and so readily absorbing substances into the body's system. It is now

**Culinary:** Fresh St John's Wort leaves were added to salads, and the fresh flowers can also be used as an edible garnish.

**Magic and myth:** It was hung in windows during the Middle Ages to ward off witches on St John's Eve (23 June) and was believed to promote good fortune and protect a house from fire. The tops of the plant were also considered effective in keeping away undesirable influences and for bringing luck. Highlanders believed that by carrying part of this plant it would protect them from witchcraft; would ward away second sight, enchantment, the evil eye and death; would help ensure peace and plenty in the house and increase growth and fruition in the field. They also thought it helped improve the yield and quality of their cows' milk if added to the milking pail.

**Modern uses:** Used to relieve the symptoms of depression, anxiety and insomnia, it is also used for skin problems, burns, wounds, bruises, sores and insect bites.

**Flowers:** June to September.

**Height:** Up to 90cm (36in). A perennial, can be grown in full sun or partial shade.

## SELF-HEAL

### Latin: *Prunella vulgaris*; Gaelic: *Slàn-lus*

Also known as Woundwort, All-heal, Heart of the Earth, Cure-all and Carpenter's Weed, Brownwort or Blue Curls. The Gaelic name s*làn-lus* means 'healing plant', and an alternative name, *dubhan ceann-chòsach*, means 'sponge-headed kidney'.

**Medicinal:** This is an ancient medicinal herb with some proven antibacterial and astringent properties. A poultice was made by

Self-heal.

pounding the fresh leaves into a paste and used as a compress for wounds, sores, burns, bruises or other skin afflictions, due to its ability to stop bleeding and speed up the healing process. In the Hebrides, the leaves were blended into an ointment with golden-rod (*Solidago virgaurea*) and butter to help heal green wounds. According to John Gerard's book *The Herball* (1597), 'There is not a better wounde herbe in the world.' Culpeper's *Complete Herbal* states: 'Where there is cause to repress the heat and sharpness of humours flowing to any sore, ulcers, inflammations, swellings, or the like, or to stay the fluxes of blood in any wound or part, this is used with some good success.' The leaves were used on their own to treat mouth ulcers and sore throats and for respiratory problems. The Gaelic names point to what was believed to be the healing properties of the plant in helping to remove all obstructions of the liver, kidney and spleen.

**Culinary:** Self-heal can be made into a herbal tea and and used to add flavour to salads, soups and stews. All parts of the herb are edible, so can be boiled and eaten as a leaf vegetable.

**Modern uses:** It is currently sold in pill and tincture form, as well as in topical balms and ointments for treating wounds and skin conditions. It is also seen as a tonic for the liver and gall bladder.

**Flowers:** June to September.

**Height:** 20cm (8in). A perennial, to be grown in full sun or partial shade. The flower heads

127

should be removed before seeds set, or it can become invasive.

## SWEET VIOLET

### Latin: *Viola odorata*; Gaelic: *Fail-chuach*

In Greek mythology Zeus had a lover named Io. His jealous wife Hera turned her into a white heifer, so Zeus created violets to give her something pleasant to graze upon. Violets were popular with the ancient Greeks, who used them to make such a popular perfume that it became the symbol of Athens. The Romans used to make violet wine, and strewed the sweet-scented flowers on floors. During the Middle Ages, monks called the violet 'an Herb of the Trinity' because they were found in the three primary colours of white, yellow and mauve/blue. Our ancestors believed these plants to be flowers of change, transition and a symbol of the cycle of death and rebirth. Violets mixed with goats' milk were used cosmetically to make a woman's skin more alluring. The Gaelic name translates as *fail* – 'scent' and *chuach* – 'a bowl'.

**Medicinal:** The leaves and flowers were made into a medicine and also used as a poultice to cool any heat or hot swellings in the body, or to soothe eye inflammations. Hildegard de Bingen's *Causes and Cures* (*c.*1151) provided a recipe for oil of violets as a cure for blurred vision. A syrup of violet flowers with honey was an effective cough remedy, used for diseases of the lungs as well as for back pain and

Sweet violet.

cystitis. Powdered flowers taken in water relieved the falling-sickness (now known as epilepsy) in children. In Scotland it was known as a treatment for headache and catarrh and recommended to be eaten after bloodletting.

**Culinary:** Violets were commonly grown in medieval kitchen gardens and its young leaves and flowers were eaten in salads. There is a fifteenth-century recipe for Vyolette, a pudding made from violet petals, almond milk and rice flour.

**Modern uses:** The flowers are high in vitamin C and good for respiratory problems. Sweet violet contains an active ingredient similar to aspirin and is therefore useful for heart health and for alleviating pain, body aches and inflammation, such as in flu symptoms or arthritis, and it is a known diaphoretic (promoting sweating), which can help to bring down a fever.

**Flowers:** Late March to April.

**Height:** 15cm (6in). A perennial, to be grown in full sun or partial shade.

## THYME

**Latin:** *Thymus vulgaris*; **Gaelic:** *Lus an rìgh*

This herb was put among household linens to repel insects. Ladies embroidered a thyme sprig in flower, along with a bee, on 'favours' for their favourite knights, as the herb was believed to bring vigour and courage to the bearer. Thyme was also used as incense and placed on coffins during funerals, as it was supposed to assure passage into the next life. It was used in baths and as an astringent. The Gaelic name *lus an rìgh* translates as 'The King's Plant'.

**Medicinal:** The essential oils within thyme contain large amounts of thymol, a strong antibacterial agent, antiseptic and antioxidant. This made it effective in the treatment of all respiratory diseases, such as chronic or acute bronchitis, upper respiratory tract inflammation and whooping cough, as well as burns and sprains. It was used to fumigate rooms against infection. The oil was used in mouthwashes to treat mouth inflammations as well as infections of the throat. Culpeper's *Complete Herbal* states that 'It purges the body of phlegm, and is an excellent remedy for shortness of breath.'

**Culinary:** Eaten raw in salads, it is also used as a condiment to flavour cooked food. The dried or fresh leaves of the thyme plant along with the flowers were used in stews and soups, sautéed or baked vegetables, custards and casseroles. It was also used in marinades and stuffings for meat. Varieties of thyme may well have been used in Scotland to flavour whisky.

**Magic and myth:** In the Middle Ages, the herb was placed beneath pillows to aid sleep and ward off nightmares. Burned as incense, it purified the home and protected its inhabitants.

**Modern uses:** Thyme is used for the relief of coughs and catarrh and for wound healing, heart, kidney and digestive health.

**Flowers:** May to October.

**Height:** 30-45cm (12-18in). Grow this dwarf shrub in full sun and cut back to the lowest green shoots in the spring to keep it bushy.

Thyme.

## Also WILD THYME or CREEPING THYME

**Latin:** *Thymus serpyllum*;
**Gaelic:** *Lus mhic rìgh Bhreatainn*

The Gaelic name means 'The Son of the King of Britain's Plant'. This had the reputation of giving courage and strength through its smell. Highlanders took it as an infusion, believing it would prevent or cure nightmares.

## WORMWOOD

**Latin:** *Artemisia absinthium*;
**Gaelic:** *Burmaid*

Other commonly used names for this herb included Felon Herb, Naughty Man and Old Uncle Henry. It was also called Sailor's Tobacco and was smoked as a tobacco substitute. Wormwood contains an essential oil with powerful insect-repellent properties. Bouquets or potpourris containing the herb were often placed in kitchens to keep flies at bay, and leaves were placed in closets and cupboards to keep moths away.

**Medicinal:** It was used in small amounts, due to its hallucinatory properties, to kill intestinal parasites. Fresh leaves were rubbed on the skin to ward off mosquitoes.

**Culinary:** A bitter aromatic herb, its leaves and roots were used as a flavouring.

**Magic and myth:** It was believed to have strong magic power against witches and the devil, and would keep the home protected. Hanging wormwood above the door was a protection against lightning, while putting it under the doorstep ensured that no threatening person would come to your door.

**Modern uses:** It is used to eliminate parasites and to improve gut health. It is also used to help stimulate appetite following illness. It is suggested that it can be helpful for people with Crohn's disease and arthritis.

**Flowers:** August to September.

**Height:** 50-100cm (20-40in). Grow this perennial in full sun and in a sheltered position.

Wormwood.

130

# YARROW

**Latin:** *Achillea millifolium*;
**Gaelic:** *Lus na fala*

Yarrow is linked to Achilles, one of legends' greatest heroes, as it was said that he used it when tending the wounds of his men. Hence, most of its common names are linked back to war – Soldier's Woundwort, Bloodwort, Staunchweed and Herbe Militaris. An alternative Gaelic name *lus chasgadh na fala* translates as 'the plant which staunches bleeding'.

It was also known to the Chinese in ancient times, with 49 yarrow stalks being used in a form of divination as set out in the *I Ching* (*Book of Changes*). Pollen from yarrow plants, among other medicinal herbs, was discovered at a burial site for a Neanderthal man (*c.*60,000 BC), indicating the importance of this plant throughout human history.

**Medicinal:** Having strong antiseptic qualities, this herb was good for the stomach, headaches, fevers, infections, mad dog bites, varicose veins, as a digestive aid, for treating the kidneys and various urinary conditions. It was also used for pain relief and as a mild sedative. Yarrow tea was taken to stop internal bleeding and mixed with mint to relieve a cold. Yarrow contains an alkaloid which helps blood clot faster, which made it a popular herb to treat battle wounds and bruises. In the Scottish Highlands, yarrow was used in healing ointments and was burnt as an insect repellent.

Yarrow.

**Culinary:** Young leaves were used in salads and infused to make a herbal tea.

**Magic and myth:** The herb was used in the casting out of witches and at one time was dedicated to the Devil. It was also associated with love, as, placed under a pillow, it could encourage dreams of sweethearts and predict the chances of marriage.

> And thrice good-morrow to thee;
> Come, tell me before to-morrow,
> Who my true love shall be.

Young girls used to take it and put it in their breasts as a charm, repeating this rhyme:

> Eerie, eerie, I do pluck,
> And in my bosom do put,
> The first young lad that speaks to me,
> The same shall my true lover be.

**Flowers:** June to August.

**Height:** 50cm (20in). Grow this perennial in full sun.

### Herbs from the Sea
(Photos by Miek Zwamborn)

As well as the berries, seeds, flowers, leaves, stems and roots of land plants, the Beatons probably collected and used seaweed as a herbal remedy for illnesses and injuries. Seaweed can be found along rocky shorelines and grows the whole year around, although each species has its own life cycle. Depending on the season it would have been directly available for the treatment of patients or dispensed from marine plants which had been preserved. Seaweed can easily be dried in the wind, sun or above an open fire to be stored for later use. Packed in airtight containers it is long lasting and lightweight as well; something that would have been quite important for the far-travelling physicians.

Seaweed draws an extraordinary wealth of mineral elements from the sea. The mineral macronutrients include sodium, magnesium, potassium, chlorine, sulphur and phosphorus; the micronutrients include iron, zinc, copper, selenium, molybdenum, fluoride, manganese, boron, nickel and cobalt. Seaweed is one of the richest plant sources of calcium as well as iodine. Red and brown seaweed contain protective pigments and many antioxidants in the form of vitamins A, C, E and B12, which are not found in most land plants.

## BLADDERWRACK
### Latin: *Fucus vesiculosus*;
### Gaelic: *Feamainn Bhoilgíneach*

Bladderwrack is named after its air bladders: balloon-like structures which help float submerged fronds up towards the water surface for photosynthesis.

**Medicinal:** This seaweed, also named Lady wrack or Black tang in former times, was used to treat an underactive thyroid gland, goitre and to cure a stitch. The jelly-like contents from the vesicles of the seaweed were used to treat sprains. Boiled up as a hot poultice it was applied to swollen joints and given internally to relieve symptoms of rheumatoid arthritis. Its rich nutritional value made it a useful herb in convalescence and for building up the body when one was weak.

**Culinary:** Bladderwrack can be used to make stock for vibrant soups or turned into a 'coat'

Bladderwrack.

for steamed fish by simply wrapping strings of seaweed around the fish and cooking it in the oven at 180 degrees. In the past the ash of bladderwrack was used to salt cheese.

**Magic and myth:** A folktale from Vatersay tells of a woman, presumably a witch, stealing the milk from cows on the beach by tying them up with a stem of Black tangle.

**Modern uses:** Bladderwrack is one of the components of Thalassotherapy. Bathing in tubs filled with heated saltwater and fresh seaweed cleanses, soothes and revitalises the skin. It also improves circulation and muscle tone.

# DULSE

### *Latin: Palmaria palmata; Gaelic: Duileasg*

The name 'Dulse' comes from the Irish/Scottish Gaelic word Dillisk, which means 'leaf from the water'.

**Medicinal:** Dulse was used for a wide range of health issues. When a large handful of dulse was rubbed on the belly of a mother during delivery, it was said that the placenta arrived safely and with great ease. The fresher the dulse, the more effective it was. Somebody suffering from colic could also be cured by placing a warm dulse pack, including its juice, on one's lower abdomen. The compress had to be changed several times a day. Externally it was used as a tonic as well as a cure for worms and skin disorders.[120] Benefits of dulse also include helping to lower blood pressure,

Dulse.

improving eyesight, improving the health of the thyroid gland, easing constipation and promoting perspiration. Eaten raw or cooked and consumed daily, it appears to have been an excellent remedy for scurvy.

**Culinary:** Fresh chopped dulse makes a very good pesto when mixed with garlic, rocket, some drops of lemon and olive oil. Fried or dry-roasted it is a good substitute for bacon, because of its tangy, smoky flavour.

**Magic and myth:** It is said that Celtic warriors ate dried dulse for stamina when on the march.[121]

In the sixth century, The Psalter Prayer of St Columba, who had established the religious community on Iona, contains the instruction, 'Gathering dulse, Catching fish, Giving food to the poor', as part of the work of his followers.

**Modern uses**: Dulse pairs well with eggs,

mushrooms, fish and starchy vegetables such as potatoes and sweet potatoes.

## IRISH MOSS/CARRAGEEN

### Latin: *Chondrus crispus*;
### Gaelic: *Cairgein, Carraigean*

The name of this fan-like small red seaweed, varying in colour from greenish-yellow, through red, to a dark purple or purplish-brown, derives from *carraig* which means 'small rock' in Gaelic, the very surface on which this seaweed grows. Another Gaelic name, *Màthair an duilisg*, means 'the mother of the dulse'.

**Medicinal:** Carrageen contains large amounts of polysaccharides, iodine and bromine. Taken for coughs and bronchitis, it was said to encourage the coughing up of phlegm and to soothe dry and irritated mucus membranes. It was also used as a demulcent[122] in gastric ulcers, to relieve both constipation and diarrhoea and to soothe inflammation in cystitis and other urinary infections. When dried and crushed, it was eaten and thought to have the same properties as cod liver oil.[123]

**Culinary:** It was used as a thickening and stabilising agent in food and cosmetics. It is also used in shoe polish, firefighting foam and for fining beer. The traditional way of preparing a pudding with carrageen is to lay the freshly cut plants out in the sun and allow it to bleach. It is recommended that it be rained upon three times, and it is said that the best surface to dry

Carrageen.

it on is a clover lawn, as the plant will absorb sweetness from the clover flowers.[124] Boiled in milk and sieved, it produces a light grey gelatinous pudding like blancmange. Mixed with vanilla, citrus or chocolate, carrageen pudding is prized for its light texture and briny, almost spicy flavour.

**Magic and myth**: In Ireland, carrageen was carried on trips for protection and safety and placed beneath rugs to increase luck and to ensure a steady flow of money into the household. Although you could certainly find carrageen growing at Sgeir a' Charraigein on the west coast of Mull, opposite the island of Ulva, its name there does not refer to the plant carrageen, but to the nearby sea-pinnacle An Carraigean: 'the skerry of the small rock'.[125]

**Modern uses:** Irish moss can be used as a vegan substitute for gelatin.

## SEA-GRAPES or GULFWEED

**Latin:** *Sargassum vulgare*;
**Gaelic:** *turusgar /trusgar*

An invasive seaweed for several decades, sea-grapes probably came originally with ballast water in ships. When the Beatons were practising, they were frequently washed across the Atlantic by the Gulf Stream, with beans, nuts and seeds, and cast up on the western shores. The sea-grapes were carefully gathered by local folk, preserved, and often worn as charms. They were called *uibhean sithein*, fairy eggs, and it was believed that they would ward off evilly disposed fairies.[126]

Sea-grapes.

Tangle.

## TANGLE / OARWEED

**Latin:** *Laminaria digitata*;
**Gaelic:** *Ceilp* or *stamh/slat-mhara*

Tangle has broad chocolate-coloured, deeply indented leaves that appear to be made up of numerous fingers (the Latin word *digitus* means 'finger').

**Medicinal**: The ashes of burned tangle were mixed with salt water and used to remove parasites from wounds. By spraying this liquid on the wound and allowing it to dry, the parasites were repelled. Chewing on tangle was known to clear heat, transform phlegm, soften hardness, and dissipate nodules. Eating it raw promoted urination and reduced oedema and was effective in treating goitre and scrofula. Extracts of tangle were also suitable for treating liver-spleen enlargement, liver cirrhosis and tumours. A poultice of tangle was used to clear warts.

135

## PINK PAINT

**Latin:** *Lithophyllum incrustans*;
**Gaelic:** *(no Gaelic name known)*

This red seaweed sticks to the rocks in a thin crust and sometimes grows among the roots of kelp. It resembles coral because of the hard calcareous deposits in its cell walls.

**Medicinal:** Long after the Beatons had ceased practising, the inhabitants of the Hebrides still scraped it from the boulders, and the seaweed, ground and mixed with egg yolk, was used as a medicine to treat diarrhoea. It was given to cattle too, especially if an animal had broken a leg, and was also used as a deworming medicine.

**Modern uses**: Medical science now uses coralline algae including pink paint in the preparation of dental bone implants. The cell fusions provide the matrix for the regeneration of bone tissue.

Pink paint.

Sea lettuce.

## SEA LETTUCE

**Latin:** *Ulva lactuca*; **Gaelic:** *Linnearach*

True to its name, the ruffled, emerald-green, translucent fronds of this seaweed resemble lettuce leaves.

**Medicinal**: The broad crinkly blades of this seaweed were used to soothe headaches. Applied to the forehead and temples they would induce sleep for patients who were recovering from fever, but were also applied for 'twisting' of the guts, treating gout and as a refreshing and cooling plaster to heal the skin after burns.[127]

**Culinary**: Despite looking flimsy, sea lettuce is strong enough to use for wrapping grilled vegetables or fish and can be used raw or cooked in salads or soups, chopped as a relish or added as a late ingredient in stir-fries.

## Some advice about how to collect, dry and preserve seaweed

If you decide to forage for seaweed around your own coasts the points below are good to bear in mind:

Do be wary of where you forage in terms of water quality, as seaweed has a knack of absorbing toxins and heavy metals.

Work out when the tide drops and plan your foraging trips accordingly to avoid getting trapped by an incoming tide.

Wear hiking shoes or gumboots with a good tread, as you will almost certainly need to clamber over rocks at some stage. Wet seaweed-covered rocks are tricky and treacherous.

Drying seaweed.

Bring a small bucket or net bag and tie it around your waist to hold your finds.

Cut fronds or blades well above the point of growth and always leave the holdfast attached to the rock bed.

Collect less than a third of an individual plant to allow for regrowth. You will only need a little seaweed for cooking.

Avoid or minimalise trampling, and avoid taking 'bycatch', like little shells, crabs etc.

Always wash sand out with seawater, and try to keep the different kinds of seaweed apart, otherwise you will end up trying to sort them out in the kitchen for a long time.

You can either eat seaweed the same day (raw or cooked), put it in the fridge for a few days or dry it in a laundry dryer to store away in a glass jar for later use. Dried seaweed can be kept for more than a year.

### A Few Recipes

#### *Vyolette*

This recipe comes from *The Forme of Cury*, one of the oldest collections of medieval English recipes, compiled *c.*1390 by the master-cooks of King Richard II. The title translates as 'The Method of Cooking' as the word 'cury' comes from the French *cuire*, to cook. In the introduction to the collection, it is explained that the recipes were meant to teach cooks how to make both common dishes and unusual banquet dishes. It is also noted that the recipes were written with the advice of experts in medicine and philosophy.

The original recipe states:

*Take Flourys of Vyolet, boyle hem, pres-se hem, bray hem smal, temper hem vppe with Almaunde mylke, or gode Cowe Mylke, a-lye it with Amyndoun or Flowre of Rys; take Sugre y-now, an putte per-to, or hony in defaute; coloure it with þe same þat þe flowrys be on y-peyntid a-boue.*

Take a cupful of violet flowers, retaining a few for decoration. Cover with a little water and bring to the boil. Immediately remove from the heat and strain off the liquid. Roughly chop the damp flowers, return to the saucepan and add a cup of milk. Reheat until simmering. Sift in 1½ tablespoons of almond or rice flour and whisk well until smooth. Add honey or 1-2 tablespoons sugar to taste. Leave on a low heat for 2 minutes until it is bubbling gently and feels as if it is thickening to a near-solid consistency. Remove from the heat and immediately pour into the serving containers. Top with the remaining violet petals and serve warm.

### Sweet Violet Tea

Add 1-2 teaspoons of chopped leaves to 1 cup of boiling water. Infuse for 10 minutes then strain.

### Yarrow Puree

Wash and dry a handful of young yarrow leaves. Boil in salted water for 20 minutes, drain and chop the leaves.

Melt a knob of butter in a small saucepan, and add the leaves with salt and pepper to taste. Fry for 5 minutes and serve.

### Winter Pottage

Often eaten at the commencement of a meal, a pottage was the forerunner to soup-making of today. A recipe would vary depending upon the vegetables and meat available at the time.

Boil together a mix of kale, mallow, sage and parsley. Add milk and almonds.

### Summer Pottage

Boil together borage, bugloss, violets and spinach and add the tops of lettuce, fennel and parsley.

### Kelp Broth

This recipe is recommended if you feel ill as it is packed with vitamins and minerals.

Heat 2 tablespoons of oil. Add 2 chopped medium onions, 5 cloves of garlic cut in small rings, 20g dried kelp seaweed (or a fresh foraged strip) cut into 3cm squares, 40g finely grated fresh ginger and 50g fresh turmeric. Stir until the onion is translucent. Add 1 litre of vegan stock. Bring to a boil, then turn down to low and simmer for 30 minutes. Turn off, let it sit for another 30 minutes and strain through a colander. Drink 3 cups of this a day.

### Duileasg Bree – Dulse Broth

Wash a handful of dulse well in running water when fresh or soak 25g of dried dulse for 30 minutes in cold water. Put the seaweed in a large pan, cover with 1.5 litre of cold water and simmer gently for 1 hour with the lid on. Add 400 ml milk, stir in 300g cooked mashed potato and simmer together for 20 minutes. Then beat in pepper, salt, a knob of butter and a little lemon juice. Add some more water or milk to dilute if the soup becomes too thick. Serves 6.

### Carrageen Cream

This recipe is similar to a pannacotta and uses a handful (7g) of dried carrageen (Irish moss) which needs to be soaked overnight before using (and makes a good gelatine substitute). Set aside six sprigs of carrageen for decoration. Boil the remaining carrageen with 40g sugar and 300ml milk in a saucepan. Stir continuously until the liquid solidifies on the back of a spoon (about 15 minutes). Remove the moss and gently stir in 300ml whipped double cream and ¼ tsp vanilla essence. Remove from the heat and leave to set in a cool place. Divide into 6 serving dishes. Top each with a sprig of carrageen and then a little sieved cocoa powder. Remove the sprigs before serving to leave a pattern on the cocoa powder.

## Try creating your own Neolithic-inspired menu

The following food items were widely available in the Highlands during the Mesolithic and early Neolithic Periods over 4000 years ago:

salted hazelnuts

brosemeal pancakes stuffed with mushrooms, juniper berries, watercress and herbs

smoked venison with a yoghurt and rowan-berry dip, laverbread and oatmeal balls

smoked salmon in pumpernickel bread

parsnip and carrot croquettes

oatcakes with crowdie

# *Appendices*

## Appendix 1
### History of the Ownership of Mull

#### 500 AD

Three Celtic clans of Irish Scotti landed in the western peninsula of Kintyre and established the kingdom of Dalriada. Their leader was Fergus Mac Erc who was descended from Conn of the Hundred Battles; he settled his people along the West Highland coastline and on the southern islands of the Inner Hebrides. They spoke Gaelic and over the next 200 years established their kingdom, driving the Picts out and giving their name to the emerging realm of Scotland (Williams, *Lords of the Isles*, p. xi).

#### 1156

Sea battle between Somerled and the Viking Godred of Man. A fragile truce was reached and lands were divided. Godred seems to have retained Mull (Williams, *Lords of the Isles*, pp. 117-118).

#### 1158

Somerled breaks the peace and takes the Isle of Man and the southern Hebrides, including Mull, by conquest (Williams, *Lords of the Isles*, pp.117-118).

#### c.1165

Ranald eldest son of Somerled and his brother Dugall are in dispute over the claim to Mull following their father's death. Ranald inherited Kintyre and Islay and all the islands south of Ardnamurchan including the disputed claim to Mull, but not the Isle of Man, which reverted to the Norse King Ragnvald. Dugall inherited Lorne, Jura, Coll and Tiree and the disputed claim to Mull. His descendants styled themselves 'de Ergadia' of Argyll, became known as the House of Lorne and later suffered forfeiture under the Bruce (Williams, *Lords of the Isles*, pp. 126-127).

#### c.1215

Ranald's son Donald kills his uncle Dugall mac Somerled in a quarrel over the continuing dispute over Mull (Williams, *Lords of the Isles*, p. 133).

#### 1300

Donald's grandson, Angus Og, inherits most of Kintyre and the disputed claim, with the House of Lorne, to Mull (Williams, *Lords of the Isles*, p. 149).

#### 1301

Macleans are sent by the House of Lorne to

prosecute their quarrel with Angus Og over Mull. The House of Lorne had previously contracted an alliance with the Comyns, and they were all enemies of the House of Bruce. The Macleans ended up kidnapping Angus Og when he was crossing the Sound of Mull to Aros. The Macleans changed allegiance and sided with Angus Og, a supporter of Robert the Bruce (Williams, *Lords of the Isles*, pp. 153-55).

### 1366

Lachlan Maclean marries the granddaughter of Angus Og and through her acquires lands in Morven and is allowed to continue living in Duart Castle (Williams, *Lords of the Isles*, p. 155).

### 1315

Robert the Bruce bestows and confirms the ancient Clan Donald lands, including Mull, on Angus Og for his faithful support during the Battle of Bannockburn (Williams, *Lords of the Isles*, p. 161).

### 1335

Edward III of England ratifies ownership of Clan Donald lands, including Mull, by John, 1st Lord of the Isles (Williams, *Lords of the Isles*, pp. 171-2).

### 1353

John, 1st Lord of the Isles, agrees that John of Lorne will hold Jura and Mull as his vassal (Williams, *Lords of the Isles*, p. 174).

### 1366

Mary, the daughter of John, 1st Lord of the Isles, marries the 5th Chief, Lachlan Maclean.

He is allowed to continue living in Duart Castle on the Isle of Mull (Williams, *Lords of the Isles*, p. 155).

### 1390

Donald, 2nd Lord of the Isles, grants custody and constableship of Duart Castle to the 5th Chief, Lachlan Maclean (MacLean, *History of the Clan MacLean*, pp. 29 and 39).

### 1493

At a Parliament in Edinburgh, possessions of the Lords of the Isles are declared forfeit to the Crown (MacLean, *History of the Clan MacLean*, p. 55).

### 1495

James IV confirms the grant by Donald, 2nd Lord of the Isles, to Hector Maclean for Duart Castle and also lands in Mull (MacLean, *History of the Clan MacLean*, p. 55).

## Appendix 2
## Beatons and the Royal Court

Patrick MacBeth of Islay, principal physician to Robert I, was employed by Crown 1306-1329 (Bannerman, p. 11).

Hector Beaton of Balgillachie, near Dundee, physician to David II, accompanied King to Battle of Neville's Cross in 1346, was employed by Crown 1346-1359 (Bannerman, p. 59).

Ferchardus Medicus Noster (Beaton of Melness, near Kyle of Tongue), granted lands and money for services as a physician to Robert II and III, was employed by Crown 1379-1397 (Bannerman, pp. 62-63).

John Leich (Beaton) of Kildavanan, Bute, granted land by James I for services as physician, was employed by Crown 1429 (Bannerman, p. 60).

David Leich (Beaton) of Kildavanan, Bute, charter confirmed by James III for services as a physician, was employed by Crown 1467 (Bannerman, p. 60).

Thomas Leich (Beaton) of Kildavanan, Bute, grant and gift of lands for service to King as physician, was employed by Crown 1488-1499 (Bannerman, pp. 60-61).

Fergus Fionn of Islay, Crown rental tenant, was employed by Crown 1506-1541, reference Bannerman, p. 12.

Henry Leich (Beaton) of Kerrylamont, Bute, accompanied James IV to Flodden and perished there with him, was employed by Crown 1513 (Bannerman, p. 61).

Fergus MacBeth of Islay, chief physician to James VI within the bound of the islands of Scotland, was employed by Crown 1567-1625 (Bannerman, p. 12).

John Beaton of Pennycross, Mull, physician to James II, also called to heal the King of Scots in a legend, was employed by Crown 1594-1657 (Bannerman, p.53, and MacKenzie, *Hereditary Physicians of the Hebrides*, 1898).

Fergus Beaton of Ballenabe, Islay, was employed by Crown 1609-1628 (Bannerman, p. 82).

David Beaton of Culnaskea, near Dingwall, physician to Charles I, was employed by Crown 1714-1763 (Bannerman, p. 74).

### Appendix 3
### The Beaton Island Divisions in the West of Scotland

Dates taken from Bannerman show known surviving primary source records indicating Beatons at these locations.

Ballenabe – Islay – 1306 to 1628, MacDonald. Beatons in Kilchoman parish from end of the fourteenth century, land grant from Donald MacDonald in 1408.

Kildavanan and Kerrylamont – Bute – 1429 to 1513. Physicians to Royal Court.

Colonsay – 1565, MacDonald.

Connista – Skye – 1660, MacDonald of Moidart.

Dervaig – Mull – 1558, MacLean.

Kilelane – Islay – 1541, MacDonald.

Pennycross – Mull – 1572, MacLean.

Portree – Skye – 1588, MacDonalds of Sleat.

Sleat – Skye – 1690, Clanranald.

Evidence of Beatons tending patients on North and South Uist from 1660, however, seem to indicate they lived on Skye under Clanranald and MacDonalds of Sleat

## Appendix 4
## A Gaelic Letter

A sixteenth-century Gaelic letter survives: correspondence between Lachlan Mòr Maclean and his doctor Malcolm Beaton.

This letter is referred to by John Bannerman and R. Black in Scottish Gaelic Studies XIII (1978), pages 56-65 and 60-61. It helps illustrate the type of relationship enjoyed by the Lord and his physician – the familiarity of the doctor-patient relationship in Gaelic society at this time. It was written in Classical Gaelic – the language used in official documents and the one in which the Beatons would have written their manuscripts, etc.

*Mile bennacht a Lochloinn Mac Mhic Giolla Eoin chum ollibh fein mar ata Giolla Colaim Maicbheath, ata se da iaraidh ort air shon fein,*

*air son a mic, tigharna Colla, fregara fa dhul dach inghean inghine Meic Cailin, do dheinibh gach maithe d'fedfis tu di. Ni beg sin ach mo bennacht chum inghine Mhic Eoin Stiufart, a cloine uile.*

*Misi Lochloinn Mac Giolla Eoin*

A thousand blessings from Lachlan [a] son of Maclean [b] to his personal physician, that is Malcolm Beaton [c], and he is wanting you for himself and her son, the Lord of Coll [d] and answer about going to MacCailean's [e] granddaughter, and doing every good you can do for her. That is no small thing (I am much obliged to you), but my blessings to the daughter of Iain Stewart [f] and all her children.

I am Lachlan Maclean[128]

The people mentioned in this letter:

a. Sir Lachlan Mór Maclean (1558-1598) was 10th Laird of Duart and 14th clan chief. He is one of the most celebrated of the clan chiefs in the annals of clan history; called Big Lachlan 'both on account of his stature and the greatness of his mind. He [129]was the most accomplished and warlike chief that ever held sway in Duart.' As such, of course, he probably often had need of his personal physician!

b. Lachlan Mór was the son of Eachuinn Og Maclean, or Hector the Younger (1529-1578) – quite a different character from his son! In the opinion of J.P. Maclean, writing in 1889, 'He should have been called Hector the Spendthrift, as during the short period of his supremacy (just five years) he spent all the ready money left by his noble father and burdened the estate with debt. He was the only worthless chief of Maclean.'[130] However, it was he who gave the lands of Pennycross to Andrew Beaton.

c. Malcolm Beaton, the second of the Pennycross personal physicians, and son of Andrew, to whom Hector the Younger had given Pennycross.

d. The Lord or Laird of Coll was the son of Lachlan Mór's sister Marion, who had married Hector Roy (Red Hector), 5th Maclean of Coll.

e. Mac Cailein is the Gaelic family name of the Campbells. Gilleasbaig MacCailein (Archibald Campbell, 4th Earl of Argyll) was the father of Seònaid (Janet) who had married Eachuinn Og Maclean (Hector the Younger).

f. One of Hector's sisters (he had seven!) was Katherine, who married John Stewart (Mac Eòin Stiùbhart) of Appin some time before 1576. It would be her grandchildren Lachlan Mór was referring to.

We also know from one of the manuscripts[131] in the Pennycross library that Malcolm Beaton was attending the house of Appin between 1593 and 96.

# Appendix 5
## A Beaton Memorial

The Argyll Archives, Inveraray Castle, hold several papers dating from the 1760s, dealing with the request made by Neil Beaton for the restitution of the Beaton lands of Pennycross. The first 'Memorial', written by or on behalf of Neil himself, gives details of the progression of events in the Beaton family from the time of the first granting of the charter in 1572 to the time of Neil's application for restitution of the Pennycross lands to the Beaton family.

There is a second, shorter Memorial, giving details of Neil's life. It is interesting to see how much Neil travelled in his early life and his wide work experience.

Transcriptions of these papers are reproduced here by permission of the Argyll Archives, Argyll Estate.

Memoriall for Neill Beaton of Piencross

The Memorialist was the third & youngest son of Mr John Beaton Minister in Mull & was only six months old at his ffathers death.

At the age of two years He was brought to Inverara where he had his education & when about 17 years of age he was put to serve Claud Fraser Barber & Wagonmaker in Inverera with whom he remained about a Twelve month, after which he came to Edinburgh where he served as a journeyman to two Master Barbers, thereafter he served, in Leith, Newcastle London and afterwards went & resided in Newtown in Montgomeryshire in Wales where he practised as a Barber surgeon having learnt to let Blood at London with a Surgeon Barber.

The Memorialist did also learn to make and spread plaisters & practised as Surgeon while he staid in Wales which was about nine years. (The Argyll Papers, NRAS 1209/1014.)

A further document gives a genealogy of the family of the Beatons of Pennycross, upon which writers about the Beatons have based their researches.

### Genealogie of The Beattons of Peinnacross in Mull 1761

20th Octr 1752

Andrew Beatton was the first of his familie that got a Right to the Lands of Peinnacross from Hector McLean then of Duart He had a son named Malcom who succeded him

Malcom had two sons, The Eldest named Donald the other John.

Donald succeded his ffather and had a son named ffergus who succeded him

John Second son to Malcom and Brother to Donald was likwise married and left three sons The oldest named John who was Minr of Kilnineuon Mull The Second Abraham the Youngest James.

ffergus Succeded his ffather Donald and left a Son named Malcom who succeded to the lands

Malcom Dying About the year 1725 or 1726 without Isue male, The Succession to Peinnacross Devolved to John who was Minr of Kilninen in Mull, But he could not get possesion of the ffarm as it was life rented by Malcom's Mother Widow of ffergus.

Mr John Minr of Kilninen left two sons the Eldest named Edmund The second named Neill who now Claims the Estate.

Mr John Minr of Kilninen died before ffergus's widow who life rented the ffarm. Upon her Death the Succession fell to Edmund Eldest son to the Minr of Kilninen who was then very young & Sir Hector McLean caused take care of him and applyed the Rents of Peinnacross for three years towards breeding him a Surgeon. He run off from his apprentisship to England where he died

Edmund being Dead, and no account of his Brother Neill who now Claims the Estate, Sir Hector McLean made a Conveyance to Lachlan McLean Merchant in Glasgow about the year 1727 or 1728 for the Sum of £100 Lachlan Intromitted with the Rents from the time the lands were Conveyed to him till the year 1753

when the late Duke of Argyll ordered Airds, his ffactor to raise the Rents in his name as belonging to him in Virtue of his right to the Estate of Duart

N: 13: It is informed that the Lands of Peinnacross are not Comprehended in the Adjudication against the Estate of Duart and that this was the reason why Sir Hector thought he had a right to make this Conveyance –

The Lands of Peinnacross payed a feu duty of 20 ... Scots to the ffamily of Duart This ffeu duty made a part of the Wadsett of Broloss and was paid to the Wadsetter till the wadsett money was paid up by the late Duke of Argyll Upon the Redemption of the Wadsett Capt Allan McLean of Broloss (now taking the tittle of Sir Allan McLean) got a Tack from his Grace off the Lands of Broloss and feu duty of Peinnacross But the Duke since first he ordered his ffactor to take possesion has intromitted with the Rents, and it has been paid for some years past since the year 1753 alongs with the Tack duty of Broloss and Exclusie of the feu duty amounts to £6.6.0. (The Argyll Papers NRAS 1209/ 1014 papers 0004_0 and 0005_0.)

## Appendix 6
## Archaeological and Botanical Surveys

Archaeological survey of the site of the Beaton Physic Garden, Pennycross, Isle of Mull, Argyll, prepared by Dr Clare Ellis of Argyll Archaeology, March 2023.

A walkover survey was undertaken on what is believed to be the remains of the physic garden established by one of the Beaton physicians of Pennycross. A substantial sub-rectangular stone enclosure was mapped, along with the probable remains of a dwelling, two stone quarries and the remains of other stone walls of a former designed landscape.

The possible garden enclosure comprises a substantial stone wall some 1.10m wide which is constructed from large blocks of basalt that form the inner and outer wall faces with a coarse rubble core; the wall only survives to a height of 0.43m. The enclosure is sub-rectangular in form, orientated NW/SE with a probable entrance on the north side near the west corner. The entrance appears to have been carved through a natural basalt outcrop which is orientated roughly E/W and which forms the northern boundary of the garden enclosure. A modern electricity pole has been placed within the southern wall. An ancient oak is located within the garden enclosure on the edge of the natural basalt outcrop, and may have been part of a wooded area which would have provided some shelter from northerly and westerly winds. The northern side of the basalt outcrop has been quarried (Site 9 on the map) and this is presumably the source of the stone for the garden enclosure. A large linear bank of spoil, a by-product of the quarry, runs parallel to the basalt outcrop along its northern side.

A platform lies on the NW side of the garden enclosure, and this may have been partially enclosed by a stony bank/wall (Site 7). Beyond this, to the south, is a second outcrop of basalt (Site 8) which has clearly been quarried with some large blocks still lying at the quarry face. On the eastern side of the garden enclosure a wall (Site 6), which is built in the same manner as that of the garden enclosure, heads eastwards. The gap between the garden enclosure and this wall is deliberate and must have enabled access into the lower ground and the wooded area. This wall appears to be part of a large enclosure (field 16 on Langland's map of 1819); the latter was clearly designated as cultivated land in the early nineteenth century.

A dwelling is depicted on Langland's map and a house platform is clearly visible at this location measuring some 14/15m NW/SE x

A plan of the garden identifying individual features (photo by C. Ellis).

4m wide (Site 3). At the NW end a low bank hints at the survival of a wall, although apart from one stray stone there is no surviving masonry. It is entirely possible that the stone has been robbed and/or cleared from the site. Just to the SW, stone appears to have been piled around a glacial erratic; some of this field clearance may have originated from the dwelling. On the south side of the surveyed area are the remains of the old road, Site 1. To the east there are the remains of stone quarry (Site 2) and to the far west the remains of a stone structure (Site 10).

## Key to the Garden Plan

1. The old road to Fionnphort. A stone track, some 2m wide, well-defined, orientated east to west. Fords a minor burn.

2. A figure of eight quarry, with two distinct quarry scoops. 10m north to south x 23m east to west, 1.5m deep.

3. A barely discernible wall 0.10m high, 1m wide. Structure only visible at the north end, some 4m wide and 6m long. The platform continues south for another 9m, so the structure could have potentially been 14/15m long. One large stone within the interior.

4. A collection of stone on the west side of a large rock, large and small stones scattered on the slope – probable clearance, no formal arrangement visible. Just to the north of the old road.

5. A rectilinear stone enclosure wall, 1.10m wide and 0.43m high. Large blocks of stone are used in its construction, these line each side with a rubble-filled core. The north side of the enclosure is defined by a natural out-crop, the wall runs up to this on the east and west sides. There is a possible entrance into the enclosure from the north, that looks as though the rock on the east side had been cut away. The enclosure is 48m north-west to south-east and 34m east-north-east to west-south-west.

6. A stone wall, straight, built with large stones on the sides and rubble core, 0.90m wide and a maximum height of 0.30m. One large stone marks the start of the wall, there is a gap between this and the east wall of the enclosure (Site 5), which looks to be a means of getting from the low ground on the north to the higher ground to the south.

7. A platform area of relatively flat ground on the west side of the enclosure (Site 5). A low pile of stone sits against the west wall of the enclosure and may be the remains of a wall that enclosed the platform. The platform measures roughly 9m east to west x 14m north to south.

8. A stone quarry, a natural linear outcrop of stone which has been quarried to a near ver-tical face; some of the large blocks prised off the face lie where they fell. There is a large hole on the south-west side of the quarry where perhaps smaller stone was extracted. 12m x 5m.

The line of the former road to Fionnphort still shows up clearly between the invasive bracken. This old road passed close by the assumed site of the Beaton dwelling and its line would probably have changed little in the preceding centuries (photo by Miek Zwamborn).

9. A linear quarry exploiting a natural linear outcrop of rock which occurs along the north edge of the enclosure (Site 5). A large linear spoil-heap lies parallel to the quarried face, this is some 2m high and up to 4m wide. A 'cave' has been created in the rock face where blocks of basalt were prised off. Presumably these were used as a source of stone for the enclosure.

10. A drystone boulder-built structure some 3.5m wide and 5.5m long, with an internal division, one room 2m long and the other 3.5m long. Set on the edge of terrace overlooking the burn. Orientated north to south.

## Tree Survey of the Beaton Garden Area, Pennycross, Isle of Mull, conducted by John Clare, March 2023.

This survey of a belt of trees at the northern boundary of an enclosure forms part of an ongoing project associated with the medieval Beaton doctors.

A series of aerial photographs of Mull was taken around 1940 and analysis of examples of an area a short distance to the west of the site shows much less native woodland and scrub than today. This indicates that for a time during the intervening period it is almost certain that there was a dearth of grazing and browsing animals such as sheep and red deer, enabling natural regeneration from the vast seed and root source of deciduous tree and shrub species that is widespread in parts of Mull to this day.

The remnants of cultivation of farmland for arable crops, which was widespread in earlier centuries, was at a very low level when these aerial photographs were taken, and declined to the point of absence in the intervening years, enabling semi-natural vegetation, predominantly bracken (*Pteridium aquilinum*), to invade and dominate large tracts.

### Vegetation

Studying the vegetation of a site on the ground today can also often assist in determining the history of management of an area, particularly in relation to native tree, herb and grass species, especially those regarded as indicator species such as those of ancient woodland and unimproved grassland. Non-native species or 'aliens' (those that did not naturally colonise the UK following the retreat of the last Ice Age), especially those plants introduced by humans for amenity or medicinal applications, can also help determine the historical management of a site.

Introduced species include trees such as sycamore (*Acer pseudoplatanus*) and non-native coniferous trees, about which much is known as to dates of introduction. Also useful in determining the historical uses of a site are introduced herb species which have persevered as garden escapees, while native plants such as stinging nettles (*Urtica dioica*), indicate areas of nutrient enrichment, and elder (*Sambucus niger*) and rowan (*Sorbus aucuparia*), were historically planted around habitations for multiple reasons. All these species can indicate locations of former dwellings and other human activity.

## Site Description

The group of trees which are the subject of this survey are growing at the northern end of the remains of a walled enclosure that is being interpreted as the site of the Beaton Doctors' medicinal garden. The eastern, western and southern walls of this enclosure are visible as the lowest remaining courses of dry-stone dykes. They surround a level, roughly rectangular, area of ground of around 37 metres wide by 50 metres long. There appear to be several former access points through these walls and the southern wall is located on a raised earth bank.

Along the northern enclosure boundary outcrop, there are the remains of a belt of trees dominated by a huge multi-limbed sessile oak (*Quercus petraea*). This tree was coppiced and then partially collapsed many years in the past. Despite this the tree is in a very healthy condition. The base of this oak is approximately 4 metres wide giving an approximate girth of 8-9 metres, meaning it is an extremely ancient specimen (the Balmaha Oak on the southern shores of Loch Lomond, which is included in the list of Heritage Trees of Scotland, has a girth of 9.73 metres at ground level). One of the limbs is around 2 metres girth at roughly 3 metres from the base, meaning that the tree may have been coppiced several hundred years ago.

The bark of the oak bole and limbs are heavily colonised with a variety of moss,

A veteran ash tree in the shelter belt
(photo by John Clare).

lichen and fern species, while the canopy of this tree covers most of the northern end of the enclosure, projecting around 17 metres southwards from the roots.

In the north-eastern corner of the enclosure is a multi-stemmed veteran ash (*Fraxinus excelsior*) with much decay and canker to the main trunk and subsidiary limbs. The state of this tree is typical of many of the ash trees on the island, which provide an extremely valuable habitat, particularly for invertebrates and birds. Further to the east and just outside the enclosure, and on the east of the possible trackway, are two standard sessile oaks, one with a girth of 2.4 metres at 1.5 metres, giving some indication of its longevity.

The Beaton Oak, Pennycross (photo by Christine Leach).

At the western end of the tree group are two relatively mature willows (*Salix sp.*), one of which may have been pollarded in the past. There is also a host of native deciduous saplings dominated by willows, but also with birch (*Betula sp.*), hazel (*Corylius avellana*) and rowan (*Sorbus aucuparia*) in a block which provides a closed canopy over the sunken area and bank to the north of the rock outcrop which forms the northern boundary of the enclosure.

There are several sycamore (*Acer pseudoplatanus*) in this tree group at the northern end of the enclosure which are relatively young saplings and are probably fairly recently self-seeded individuals from adjacent sycamore tree groups.

The ground vegetation below the trees is typical of a grazed, secondary woodland habitat, with species such as lesser celandine (*Ranunculus ficaria*), primrose (*Primula vulgaris*) and a variety of grass and moss species. There is also a significant leaf litter, predominantly from willow and oak, that may be persisting in this location due to a lack of worms and other leaf-eating invertebrates. The main southern area of the enclosure south of the barbed-wire fence is almost entirely dominated by bracken (*Pteridium aquilinum*).

This area below the trees is open to grazing animals, and there are signs, including droppings and browsing of trees, that red deer and Highland cattle use the area for lying up in shelter that the trees provide. This means that for as long as the barbed-wire fence has been derelict, most, if not all, natural tree regeneration would have been grazed and browsed out.

## Conclusion

The group of trees along the northern boundary of the enclosure largely comprise native tree species that could have established naturally or been planted to act as a shelter belt for the walled enclosure to the south. The group stands in a relict parkland landscape where most tree groups are made up of non-native species, mainly sycamore, beech and conifers.

The large, coppiced sessile oak at the heart of this group is of significant age and indicates that it has been undisturbed for a significant time, at least in excess of several hundred years. The size of the latest coppice regrowth, in itself, is likely to indicate that it was well over a hundred years since the tree was managed. The immense size of the root bole indicates many years of growth prior to that, possibly having been coppiced many times, even taking it back to the 1600s and the time of the Beaton Doctors. This sessile oak is the oldest tree I have seen on Mull. In a recent article in the *Newsletter* of the Native Woodland Discussion Group, the oak tree has now been officially named The Beaton Oak.

All the trees within this block, especially willow and oak, have numerous medicinal uses, as well as providing wood for construction, burning and other purposes.

"Kilfinichen, Ben More and the Penny Cross in 1902" (painting by Colin McVean, 1838–1912). Colin A. McVean, son of the Iona Minister Rev. Donald McVean, trained as a civil engineer and worked on the Admiralty Survey of the Hebrides in 1861. In 1868 he was one of three engineers sent to superintend the erection of lighthouses in Japan, and by 1870 he had been appointed Surveyor-in-Chief of Japan, carrying out detailed surveys of Kyoto and Tokyo and establishing a Meteorological Office. When he returned to Mull, he settled in Kilfinichen, where he and his family were well-known and respected. His artistic ability was passed on to his children – work by two of his daughters, Flora and Iona, is also featured in this book. Reproduced by kind permission of Colin Houston.

# Bibliography

Argyll, The Duke of, *Scotland as It Was and as It Is*, Edinburgh, David Douglas, 1887.

Bannerman, J., *The Beatons, A Medical Kindred in the Classical Gaelic Tradition*, Edinburgh, John Donald, 1998.

Beath, M., *Healing Threads: Traditional Medicines of the Highlands and Islands*, Edinburgh, Polygon, 1995.

Cameron, J., *The Gaelic Names of Plants*, Glasgow, J. Mackay, 1900.

Campbell, J.L. and Thomson, D., *Edward Lhuyd in the Scottish Highlands 1699-1700*, Oxford, Clarendon Press, 1963.

Carmichael, A., *Carmina Gadelica – Hymns and Incantations*, Edinburgh, Floris Books, 1992.

Culpeper, N., *Culpeper's Complete Herbal*, first published in 1653, later edition London, Foulsham, 1880.

Darwin, T., *The Scots Herbal: The Plant Lore of Scotland*, Edinburgh, Mercat Press, 1996.

Dioscorides, Pedanius, *De Materia Medica* (written in the first century AD, this was available in medical manuscripts from the fifteenth or sixteenth centuries), source: internet archive.

Duffy, S. (ed.), *The World of the Galloglass, Kings, Warlords and Warriors in Ireland and Scotland, 1200-1600*, Dublin, Four Courts Press, 2016.

Gerard, John, *Gerard's Herball* (first published 1597), London, G. Howe, 1927.

Grace, P., *Medicine in Gaelic Ireland and Scotland, 1350-c.1750*, Irish Historical Studies Publications Ltd., 2020.

Grant, I.F., *Highland Folk Ways*, London, Routledge, 1961.

Grieve, Mrs M., *A Modern Herbal*, London, Jonathan Cape, 1931.

Hamilton, D., *The Healers: A History of Medicine in Scotland*, Edinburgh, Canongate, 1981.

Hardie, R.P., *The Tobermory Argosy: A Problem of the Spanish Armada*, Edinburgh, Oliver and Boyd, 1912.

Harington, Sir John, *Regimen Sanitatis Salernum with the Englishman's Doctor, An Ancient Translation*, with introduction and notes by Croke, Sir Alexander, Edinburgh, Royal College of Physicians, 1830. Digital edition in the Wellcome Collection.

MacGregor M., *Floodtide and a Thousand Sails (Làn-mara's mile seòl): Gaelic Scotland and Gaelic Ireland in the later Middle Ages*, University of Glasgow, 2000.

Mackechnie, Rev. J. (ed.), *The Dewar Manuscripts, Vol. 1 Scottish West Highland Folk*

*Tales collected by John Dewar for George Douglas VIIIth Duke of Argyll*, Glasgow, MacLellan, 1964.

MacKenzie, Alexander, *History of the MacDonalds and Lords of the Isles,* Inverness, A. & W. MacKenzie, 1881.

MacKinnon, D. *The Genealogy of the MacBeths or Beatons of Islay and Mull, The Caledonian Medical Journal* 1904, pp.141-153.

MacKinnon, D., *A Descriptive Catalogue of Gaelic Manuscripts*, Edinburgh, William Brown, 1912.

MacLaren, Alastair (Ed.), *Argyll, Volume 3, Mull, Tiree, Coll and Northern Argyll*, RCAHMS, Edinburgh, HMSO, 1980.

MacLean, J.P., *A History of the Clan Maclean, from Its First Settlement at Duard Castle in the Isle of Mull, to the Present Period, including a Genealogical Account of Some of the Principal Families,* Cincinnati, Robert Clarke & Co, 1889.

MacLean, J.P., *History of the Island of Mull*, Vol.1, Chap. XI, Medicine, Greenville, Ohio, Frank H. Jobes & Son, 1923.

Maclean-Bristol, N. (ed.), *Inhabitants of the Inner Isles, Morven and Ardnamurchan*, first published 1716, Edinburgh, Scottish Record Society, 1998.

MacPhail, J. (ed), *Highland Papers*, Vol 1, Edinburgh, Scottish History Society, 1914.

Martin Martin, *A Description of the Western Islands of Scotland*, London, 1703.

McCormick, J., *The Island of Mull: Its History, Scenes and Legends*, Glasgow, Alex. McLaren & Sons, 1923.

McNeill, F.M., *The Silver Bough* (A Four Volume Study of the National and Local Festivals of Scotland) Volume I, *Scottish Folk-Lore and Folk Belief*, Glasgow, William MacLellan, 1957.

McPhee, I., *The Naked Clansmen on Mull and Iona, 1700-1860*, Kibworth Beauchamp, Matador, 2020.

Mitchell Dr R., *Hereditary Physicians in Celtic Medicine*, Royal College of Physicians of Edinburgh website, *rcpe.ac.uk/heritage/hereditary-physicians-celtic-medicine.*

Muir, T.S., *Characteristics of Old Church Architecture etc in the Mainland and Western Islands of Scotland,* Edinburgh, Edmonston & Douglas, 1861. Kessinger Legacy Reprints.

Nelson J.M. (ed.), *A Mull Home Companion*, Isle of Mull, Carra Print Workshop, 1977.

Nicolson, A., *The McBeths – Hereditary Physicians of the Highlands*, Transactions of the Gaelic Society of Glasgow, 1958, pp. 94-112.

Ross, Duncan, *The Passionate Grower's Guide to Herb Gardening*, Duncan Ross, 2022.

Sinclair, A.M., *The Clan Gillean*, Charlottetown: Haszard and Moore, 1899.

Sutherland, James, *Hortus Medicus Edinburgensis*, Edinburgh, 1683. Source: internet archive.

Turner, William, *A New Herball*, first published in 1568, Cambridge University Press, 1996.

Whyte, H., *Medicinal Plants found in the Scottish Highlands, and the Purposes to Which They Were Applied*, Glasgow, *Caledonian Medical Journal*, July1904, pp. 8-14.

Whyte Rev. Thomas, (attributed to) *An Historical and Genealogical Account of the Bethunes of the Island of Sky*, London, A. Chilver, 1893.

Williams, R., *The Lords of the Isles, the Clan Donald and the Early Kingdom of the Scots*, Isle of Colonsay, House of Lochar, 1997.

Zwamborn, M., *The Seaweed Collector's Handbook*, London, Profile Books, 2020.

# Endnotes

1. Magnússon, E., *Notes on Shipbuilding and Nautical Terms of Old in the North*, p. 221.
2. Williams, R., *The Lords of the Isles: The Clan Donald and the Early Kingdom of the Scots*, pp. 117-118.
3. *Battlefields of Britain* available at *www.battlefieldsofbritain.co.uk/battle_largs_1263.html*; Williams, *The Lords of the Isles*, pp. 138-140, 161-162, 212-213.
4. Williams, *The Lords of the Isles*, pp. xiii, 127, 132, 139-141.
5. Beith, M., *Healing Threads, Traditional Medicines of the Highlands and Islands*, pp. 49-50; Williams, *The Lords of the Isles*, pp. 211-213, 215-216.
6. Mackenzie, A., *History of the MacDonalds and Lords of the Isles: With Genealogies of the Principal Families of the Name*, pp. 43-44; Bannerman, J., *The Beatons, A Medical Kindred in the Classical Gaelic Tradition*, pp. 8-10; Beith, *Healing Threads,* p. 45; Williams, *The Lords of the Isles*, pp. 169-170, 216.
7. Bannerman, *The Beatons*, p. 11; Beith, *Healing Threads*, p. 50; Williams, *The Lords of the Isles*, pp. 169-170, 216; Mackenzie, *History of the MacDonalds and Lords of the Isles,* pp. 43-44.
8. Williams, *The Lords of the Isles*, pp. 153-155, 157-161. Mackenzie, *History of the MacDonalds and Lords of the Isles*, pp. 39-44.
9. Williams, *The Lords of the Isles*, pp. 215-216; Bannerman, *The Beatons*, p. 18.
10. Bannerman, *The Beatons*, pp. 11, 26; Beith, *Healing Threads*, pp. 50-51.
11. Bannerman, *The Beatons*, p. 15.
12. Bannerman, *The Beatons*, pp. 11-12, 13-54; Williams, *The Lords of the Isles*, p. 216.
13. Bannerman, *The Beatons*, p. 82.
14. Williams, *The Lords of the Isles*, pp. xiii; Bannerman, *The Beatons*, p. 25; Beith, *Healing Threads*, pp. 49-50.
15. The beginning of the Stone Age coincides with the discovery of the oldest known stone tools, which have been dated to some 3.3 million years ago. It is divided into three separate periods, the Palaeolithic (roughly to 10,000 BC), the Mesolithic (*c.*10,000 to 4000 BC) and Neolithic (*c.*4000 to 2500 BC) based on the degree of sophistication in the fashioning and use of tools. *Encyclopaedia Britannica*.
16. Lietava. J., *Medicinal plants in a Middle Palaeolithic grave (Shanidar IV?)*, National Library of Medicine.
17. *Orkneyology.com, Skara Brae, An Ancient Village in the Heart of Neolithic Orkney*.
18. Darwin, T., *The Scots Herbal*, p. 11.
19. In Britain, this was roughly between 800 BC and 43 AD, when the Romans arrived. Cunliffe, B., *Britain Begins*.
20. The accepted meaning of the name Rossal (from the Norse) is 'Horse Field', Maclean, C., *The Isle of Mull, Placenames, Meanings and Stories*, p. 32. However, there is a theory that the name comes from the Gaelic, signifying judgment, justice.
21. Wilkinson, S., *Early Medical Education in Ireland*, Irish Migration Studies in Latin America, Vol 6, no.3, Nov. 2008.
22. One of the legendary kings of Scotland, listed in Buchanan, G., *The History of Scotland: from the Earliest Accounts of That Nation, to the Reign of King James VI,* London, 1690.
23. Livingston W.C., *Vindication of the Celtic Character: or, The Scotchman as He Was and as He Should Be, Letters,* 1850, p. 573.
24. Mitchell Dr R., *Hereditary Physicians in Celtic Medicine* (Royal College of Physicians).
25. Grace, P., *Medicine in Gaelic Ireland and Scotland, c.1350-c.1750*, p. 207.
26. Carrigan, W., *The History and Antiquities of the Diocese of Ossory*, Vol II, Dublin, Sealy, Bryers & Walker, 1905.
27. Simms, K., *Gaelic Culture and Society* in Smith, B. (ed.), *The Cambridge History of Ireland,* Vol. 1,

*600–1550*, Cambridge University Press, 2018, pp. 415–440.

28. Grace, P., *Medicine in Gaelic Ireland and Scotland, c.1350-c.1750.*

29. Beith, M., *Healing Threads*, pp. 46-48, 55-57.

30. Hendrie, A., *The Four Humours: Understandings of the Body in Medieval Medicine*, Retrospect Journal, Edinburgh University's History, Classics and Archaeology Magazine, 2021. *https://retrospectjournal.com/2021/05/02/the-four-humours-understandings-of-the-body-in-medieval-medicine/*

31. One such was *An Irish Materia Medica* by Tadhg Ó Cuinn (1415), ed. Färber. Many of his plant simples and products are still relevant or at least were used until relatively recently.

32. Excerpts from *Rosa Anglica* in various Gaelic manuscripts are available online at Irish Scripts on Screen, *https://www.isos.dias.ie* .

33. Croke, Sir A., *Regimen Sanitatis Salernitanum with the Englishman's Doctor, an Ancient Translation*, p. 24.

34. Grace, P., *Medicine in Gaelic Ireland and Scotland, c.1350-c.1750.*

35. Bannerman, J., *The Beatons*, p. 79.

36. Martin, M., *A Description of the Western Islands of Scotland circa 1695.*

37. Wormald, J., *Court, Kirk, and Community: Scotland, 1470–1625*, Edinburgh University Press, 1991.

38. Bannerman, J., *The Beatons*, p. 26, confirmed by a fuller inventory of Pennycross writs in the Saltoun Collection, Box 410 (NLS).

39. The term 'feu' means a perpetual property granted by a feudal superior to a vassal, on his continuing to pay a certain stipulated sum annually. See Murray, A., *The Procedure of the Scottish Exchequer in the Early Sixteenth Century*, *The Scottish Historical Review*, Vol. XL, No. 130, Part 2, Oct. 1961, pp. 89-117.

40. Saltoun Papers MS17678 Item 21, on a sheet numbered 1-6, on the outside of which is written *Progress of the Writs of the Lands of Pennycross in Mull possessed by Lauchlan McLean 1752.*

41. Muir. T.S., *Characteristics of Old Church Architecture Etc in the Mainland and Western Island of Scotland*, 1861, p. 147.

42. Bannerman, J., *The Beatons: A Medical Kindred*, p. 26

43. Muir, T.S., *Characteristics of Old Church Architecture Etc.* The Miss Maclean referred to was most likely Miss Julia Maclean, sister of Alexander, 3rd Maclean of Pennycross, who was living at Pennyghael (on what was at that time rather confusingly known as Pennycross Farm).

44. Johnson, S., and Boswell, J., *A Journey to the Western Islands of Scotland and the Journal of a Tour to the Hebrides.*

45. Sinclair Dr. C., *The Thatched Houses of the Old Highlands*, Oliver & Boyd, Edinburgh, 1953, p. 16.

46. Carmichael, A., *Carmina Gadelica* is a collection of hymns and incantations collected in the Highlands and Islands of Scotland. First published 1899. There is however some confusion over the Gaelic name 'mòthan'. *Flora Celtica* (Milliken, William and Bridgewater, Sam), suggests that in fact the 'mòthan' was the butterwort, or bog violet, one of the most important plants in Hebridean folklore.

47. Memories from Bertie Black, Pennycross Cottage and Jenny Watson, the Old Smiddy, Pennyghael, given to Christine Leach in 1998.

48. Mary Beith, who wrote *Healing Threads, Traditional Medicines of the Highlands and Islands*, visited the site of the Beaton garden in 1995 and suggested that the belt of trees to the north of the walled area was probably planted specifically as a shelter belt.

49. Bannerman, J., *The Beatons*, p. 26.

50. See later chapter, *The Beaton Library – NLS Adv. MS 72.1.33*, where this letter is discussed more fully.

51. Hardie, R.P., *The Tobermory Argosy, A Problem of the Spanish Armada*, 1912; also Martin, Dr. P., RCAHMS (Canmore), 2002.

52. State Papers (Scotland), Elizabeth, xlii, 119, as quoted by R.P. Hardie.

53. From Captain Charles Eggerton to the Lord Deputy, Feb. 1589. State Papers (Ireland), Elizabeth, cxli, 19.

54. Martin, M., *A Description of the Western Islands of Scotland circa 1695 – Mull.*

55. Memorial by Neill Beaton, 1760-61. See Appendix 4.

56. NLS, Advocates MS 72.1.33.

57. The advice of Professor Dame Rosemary Cramp,

DBE, FSA, FBA, is that this is the sort of cross that is impossible to date.

58. The British Lichen Society, *britishlichensociety.org.uk.*

59. Muir, T.S., *Characteristics of Old Church Architecture Etc.* p. 145.

60. Dunvegan Papers, Box 14C.

61. NLS, Advocates MS. 72.1.29,f.13v. The final figure of the year date is smudged, but according to Bannerman appears more like a 4 than anything else.

62. MacTavish, D.C. (Ed), *Minutes of the Synod of Argyll*, I, Scottish History Society, p.202.

63. Muir, T.S., *Characteristics of Old Church Architecture Etc.*, p. 147 footnote.

64. For instance there is a well-known story of Maclean of Duart marooning his wife, a sister of Argyll, on the Lady Rock.

65. For a detailed history of this time, see MacPhail, J.R.N., *Highland Papers Vol 1*, Scottish History Society, 1914.

66. Laing Manuscript, La.III.21, Edinburgh University. See chapter on The Beaton Library

67. Bannerman, J., *The Beatons*, pp. 32-33. Also, *Register of Testaments. The Commissariat Record of the Isles*, Scottish Record Office, CC 12/3/2/ p. 52.

68. RCAHMS, *Inventory of the Ancient and Historical Monuments of Argyll, Vol 4, Iona*, 1982.

69. Horning was a penal diligence for debt. A creditor obtained letters of horning directing officers of the law to charge the debtor to pay: if the latter failed, the officer blew three blasts with a horn at the appropriate market-cross and then published the fact, which constituted denunciation at the horn. Gibb, A.D., *Students' Glossary of Scottish Legal Terms*, 1946. Also, MacPhail, J. (Ed), *Highland Papers Vol. 1*

70. Martin, M., *A Description of the Western Islands of Scotland.* Also Sinclair, A.M., *The Clan Gillean*, p. 206.

71. Campbell, J.L., and Thomson, D., *Edward Lluyd in the Scottish Highlands 1699-1700*, p. 22.

72. Scott. H., *Fasti Ecclesiae Scoticanae*, p. 114.

73. NLS, Advocates MS. 72.1.3,f.98r., written in 1677.

74. *The Register of the Privy Council of Scotland, 1877*, 3rd ser. viii (1683-4), pp. 93-5.

75. The Act of Settlement was passed in 1701, reinforcing the Bill of Rights agreed by William and Mary in 1689, the main aim of which was to ensure a Protestant succession to the English throne. Later in 1707, as a result of the Act of Union, this Act was extended to Scotland.

76. Presbyterian churches were governed by representative assemblies of elders; the Episcopalian Church had bishops in its organisational structure.

77. Scott. H., *Fasti Ecclesiae Scoticanae*. It is interesting that the (extraordinarily brief) entry in *Fasti* states that he was 'outed (probably deposed) for immoral conduct in 1701'. In the light of later research it has been suggested that this unsupported statement was a political device to ensure his dismissal.

78. Nicolson, W., *Scottish Historical Library*, London 1702, p. 67.

79. Campbell, J.L., and Thomson, D., *Edward Lluyd in the Scottish Highlands 1699-1700*. The survey Lluyd undertook was a stupendous task which has never yet been completed, research still continues on every aspect of it; in several ways he was nearly two centuries ahead of his time.

80. Additional M.S. 15582 held in the British Library.

81. Campbell, J.L., and Thomson, D., *Edward Lluyd*, p. 22.

82. Campbell, J.L., and Thomson, D., *Edward Lluyd*, p. 33, quoting correspondence between John Maclean and Robert Woodrow, 1701-2.

83. Maclean-Bristol, N. (Ed), *Inhabitants of the Inner Isles, Morvern and Ardnamurchan 1716*, Scottish Record Society, Vol 21, 1998, p. 33.

84. MacLean, J.P., *A History of the Clan MacLean; from Its First Settlement at Duard Castle in the Isle of Mull, to the Present Period*, 1889, p. 214.

85. *Genealogie of the Beatons of Peinnacross*, NRAS 1209/10.14, papers 0004_0 and 0005_0, Argyll Papers, Argyll Archives, Inveraray Castle.

86. *Ibid.*

87. Lochbuie Papers, Scottish Record Office, GD174.133/11.

88. Lochbuie Papers, Scottish Record Office, GD 174/133/5.

89. Argyll Papers, Inveraray Castle, 5654/67/2/65/5.

90. To 'hough' or hamstring an animal is to cut its Achilles tendon, a quick method of crippling it.

91. Argyll Papers, NRAS1209/3073/8-9, Copy Summons Neil Beaton – Lachlan McLean, 1762.

92. Bannerman, J., *The Beatons*, p. 33 and Lochbuie Papers GD174/133/5.

93. Later he mentioned that Edmund had died in Jamaica in either 1758 or 1759. Lochbuie Papers GD174/133/11.

94. Lochbuie Papers GD174/133 contains many papers concerned with this case; from the Argyll Papers, Inveraray Castle, come another set of documents, NRAS 1209/3073/10-11 and NRAS 1209/1014. These last include the partial genealogy and a brief description of Neil Beaton's own life story. See Appendix 4.

95. £200 sterling in 1764 is the equivalent of £46,669.40 in 2023.

96. Argyll Papers, NRAS 1209/3073/8-9.

97. Documentation concerning the whole case presented by Neil Beaton against Lachlan MacLean of Glasgow and John Mclean of Killean can be found in the Lochbuie Papers GD174/133/ 12.

98. Lochbuie Papers 174/148. Also MacLean-Bristol, N., 'The Beatons' from *Notes and Queries*, No.ix (1979), p. 27.

99. Bannerman, J., *The Beatons*, p. 49.

100. This is according to Mr James Fraser, minister of Kirkhall 1662-1709, Fraser, J., *Chronicles of the Frasers*, Scottish History Society, 1905, Wardlaw MSS., pp.145-6.

101. NLS, Adv. MS 72.1.3,f. 83 r.

102. NLS, Adv. MS 18.2.11

103. Catalogue of Gaelic Manuscripts in the National Library of Scotland, MS 2076, described as a Medical Manuscript.

104. Scottish Record Office, Church of Scotland Records, CH 2/493/1.

105. Nicholson, A., *The McBeths, Hereditary Physicians of the Highlands*, Transactions of the Gaelic Society of Glasgow, 1958, p. 101.

106. One of these is Logan, J., *The Beauties of Gaelic Poetry and Lives of the Highland Bards*, Blair collection, NLS, and is called 'Iorram do Sheumas Peutan, iarogha do'n Ollamh Mhuileach' (The lament of James Beaton, great grandson of the Mull Doctor).

107. Taken from *Tocher* No 24, School of Scottish Studies, 1976 (SA 1973/67 A5).

108. This legend is related by Maclean, J.P., *History of the Island of Mull*; also by Capt. Dugald MacCormick of Ross of Mull (*Tocher* No 25, SA 1952/49BB); and by MacCormick, J., *The Island of Mull, Its History, Scenes and Legends*.

109. The manuscripts from the Scottish Record Offfice described in this chapter can be studied on the website Irish Script on Screen, *https://www.isos.dias.ie/*. Images in great detail of every folio are available and the descriptive notes by Ronald Black are given for each manuscript.

110. Gillies, G.C., *Regimen Sanitatis*, the Celt Project, University College Cork, available at *https://celt.ucc.ie/published/G600010.html*.

111. Beith, M., *Healing Threads, Traditional Medicines of the Highlands and Islands*, p. 61.

112. Bannerman, J., *The Beatons*, pp. 49, 66; also Irish Script on Screen, *https://www.isos.dias.ie/*.

113. In Roman literature, Erictho or Erichtho was a legendary Thessalian witch, perhaps created by the poet Ovid, but who appears in several works and was noted for her horrifying appearance.

114. Bannerman, J. and Black, R., *A Sixteenth-century Gaelic Letter*, Scottish Gaelic Studies, xiii, pt 1, 1978, pp. 56-65.

115. The medieval Gaelic is taken from Cox, R.A.V., ed., and Ó Baoill, C., *Ri Linn nan Linntean: Taghadh de Rosg Gàidhlig*, Clann Tuirc, 2005. Translation into English by Sarah Mawhinney.

116. Edinburgh University Library Special Collections available at *https://archives.collections.ed.ac.uk/repositories/2/resources/85248*.

117. MacKinnon, D., *A Descriptive Catalogue of Gaelic Manuscripts*, pp. 283-286.

118. Campbell, Rev. D., *First Statistical Account for Kilfinichen and Kilvickeon*, 1795.

119. 'Bluebird' relates to birds with blue colouring, but it is also the old country name for swallows and house martins which have a blue sheen to their plumage.

120. M.R. Macdonald, 'Heredity in the Scottish Highlands', *Caledonian Medical Journal*, July 1904, p.14.

121. *www.seaveg.com*, What is Dulse? Ecology and

Human History of *Palmaria Palmata*.

122. A substance that relieves irritation of the mucous membranes by forming a protective film.

123. Beliefs and practices in health and disease from the Maclagan Manuscripts (1892–1903), PhD thesis by Allan R. Turner, 2014, p. 271. The University of Edinburgh.

124. Carragheen, *www.nature.scot*, 26.07.2021.

125. Carragheen, *www.nature.scot*, 26.07.2021.

126. Cameron, John, *The Gaelic Names of Plants* (Edinburgh, Blackwood, 1883).

127. Beliefs and practices in health and disease from the Maclagan Manuscripts (1892–1903), PhD thesis by Allan R. Turner, 2014, p. 257. The University of Edinburgh.

128. Translation by Sarah Mawhinney.

129. MacLean, J.P., *A History of the Clan McLean*, p. 91

130. *Ibid.* p. 90.

131. Advocates' Library MS 72.1.3.

# *Acknowledgements*

This book did not come about overnight. It started life when Pennyghael in the Past Historical Archive decided to become involved with the Adopt-a-Monument scheme (part of Archaeology Scotland), as it had been discovered that the Beaton Cross needed urgent conservation work and we needed expert help. It became clear over the next months that the very existence of the Cross was one of the best-kept secrets on Mull, let alone the remains of the Physic Garden close by. Certainly the name of Beaton was not unknown – there have always been Beatons living on Mull – but as for the 'celebrated physicians of Pennycross', their names were unknown, except to those who had read John Bannerman's book, The Beatons (a book which, I may say, became our 'Bible').

Once our interest in the remnants of the garden and the men themselves had been piqued, it was not long before a small group of us had the idea of mounting an exhibition, to be put on in the Community Hall at Pennyghael. Andrea Cameron, Christine Leach, Miek Zwamborn and Rutger Emmelkamp were the prime movers in this enterprise, but many more folk were involved in the project. Then, a month or so before our scheduled opening, came COVID.

It was nearly two years after this that Andrea and Christine got together again and decided not to let all the hard work go to waste. The time spent on exhibition preparation was irrevocably lost, but too much time had been spent on research for us to forget the subject altogether. Also, our interest had not faded – we still wanted to tell the story. So we started again, this time with a publication in mind. We quickly discovered how different a project this was, and have been learning ever since. We have been grateful to so many people who have helped, either directly or indirectly, by lending their time and knowledge, expertise and enthusiasm, or simply encouragement. To begin with, we are indebted to Judy Gibson from Erraid, for introducing us to Elizabeth Carter, who became the fourth collaborator in the writing team. Our thanks go to those who helped us with research; Alison Diamond, Archivist of the Argyll Papers, Inveraray; Jack Green from the Centre for Research Collection, Main Library, University of Edinburgh; Dr Ulrike Hogg, of the Archives and Manuscript Collections, National Library of Scotland; Estela Dukan, from the Royal College of Physicians of Edinburgh; Jane Knowles, of the Royal College of Physicians' Medicinal Plant

Garden, London; Betty McDermott and Elin Crotty from the Centre for Research Collections, University of Edinburgh Archives; and Bob Allan, who was a never-failing source of help. We are grateful to those who have provided us with photographs and sketches, especially Nicola and Jack Welsh, Nigel Burch and Graham Kent. The model birlinn was created especially for us by Philip Siddall (and can now be seen on display at the Isle of Mull Museum, Tobermory). Colin Houston and Mark Le May kindly gave us permission to use images from their own family collections and the Glaisher family have allowed us to use sections of the Langlands estate map of Pennyghael, dated 1817, which clearly shows the Physic Garden. Clare Ellis of Argyll Archaeology did a wonderful job on the survey of the Beaton Garden, under very difficult conditions, and John Clare prepared a most detailed tree survey of the area, both of which have added greatly to the project. As non-Gaelic speakers, we have been greatly helped with the intricacies of the Gaelic language by Dr Alasdair Whyte and Jane Brunton, and to Sarah Mawhinney for her translation of the sixteenth-century 'Gaelic Letter'. Finally, we wish to thank those friends and associates who have given unstintingly of their advice, general knowledge and encouragement along the way, including Rutger Emmelkamp, Lynne Farrell, Rosalind Jones, Peter Leach, Jean Whittaker, and the Poyntzfield Herb Nursery.

# The Authors

**Christine Leach** moved to Mull more than 30 years ago to work at the YMCA Outdoor Centre at Tavool. She established Pennyghael in the Past Historical Archive and, with a group of like-minded enthusiasts, set about exploring and recording the remains of townships in the Brolas area.

**Andrea Cameron** is an archivist and local historian. She has worked in local authority and private archives in Northumberland and completed local history projects in both Northumberland and the Isle of Mull.

**Miek Zwamborn** is a Dutch author and visual artist based on Mull where she co-runs the creative hub KNOCKvologan and is involved in the re-wilding project Tireragan. She has published *The Seaweed Collector's Handbook* (Profile Books, 2020), novels, poetry pamphlets and many art books.

**Elizabeth Carter** has been gardener at Bolton Castle, Yorkshire since 2015, where she has replanted the herb garden, now containing over 100 species of plants. She is also a complementary therapist and advanced practitioner using Bach Flower Remedies. She is author of the children's book *The Adventures of Duck Bill and Arnold*.